FIFTH PUBLICATION OF THE PENNSYLVANIA SOCIETY
OF THE COLONIAL DAMES OF AMERICA

Three Centuries of Historic Silver

Loan Exhibitions under the Auspices of the
Pennsylvania Society of the Colonial
Dames of America

Compiled and Edited

By

MRS. ALFRED COXE PRIME, *Chairman*

PHILADELPHIA
PRINTED FOR THE SOCIETY
1938

THE SCIENCE PRESS PRINTING COMPANY
LANCASTER, PENNSYLVANIA

SILVER BOOK PUBLICATION COMMITTEE

Mrs. Alfred Coxe Prime, Chairman
Miss Emily Hinds Bache
Mrs. Henry Paul Baily
Mrs. Edgar Wright Baird
Mrs. Richard Standish Francis
Mrs. Harrold Edgar Gillingham
Mrs. Charles Price Maule
Miss Martha B. Newkirk
Mrs. Thornton Oakley
Mrs. Henry Burnett Robb
Miss Francis Katherine Talbot
Mrs. John Madison Taylor

"A thing of beauty is a joy forever."

Keats.

FOREWORD

The early loan exhibitions held at the Museum of Fine Arts at Boston in 1906 and 1911, together with that held at The Metropolitan Museum of Art in 1909, made America conscious of the high quality of her native silversmiths in those localities. Philadelphians did not become fully aware of their silver heritage until the 1921 exhibition was held at Memorial Hall, in which emphasis was placed largely on the styles current in the Federal period for which Philadelphia is so justly noted. But it was not until the 1929 and 1937 loan exhibitions, sponsored by the Colonial Dames, that the full development of the craft in the Quaker City could be traced ab urbe condita through the lavishness of the rococo into the glorious Federal phase and final decline during the early Victorian period. The importance of these exhibitions becomes more apparent with the publication of a lasting record of these pieces with their historic associations, which will prove to be of great value to the research students and historians of the future. A great debt of gratitude is owed to the Pennsylvania Society of the Colonial Dames of America for making possible these exhibitions and to Mrs. Alfred Coxe Prime who has given so unstintingly of her care and time in the compilation of this book.

JOHN MARSHALL PHILLIPS

INTRODUCTION

There is charm, personality and romance inevitably linked with old silver. Anything made up to the first quarter of the 19th century, as a rule, was an individual order. The silversmith hammered it out with brain and brawn—so that something of himself went into each piece he fashioned.

More romance was fused in, because most of the articles were made from silver coins: Mexican dollars, English Guineas, French Pistoles, Johannes's, Spanish Pistole Pieces, Moydores, Doubloons and pieces of Eight.

Frequently the customer brought his coins with him to the silversmith; savings, to be invested in the resulting porringers, teapots, or tankards instead of stocks and bonds, unheard of at that time. They were assets more tangible and lasting perhaps as in time of need they were frequently (alas) melted down and turned back once more into coin.

It is interesting to know something about the men who made our silver—when they lived, where, and if possible, their working dates. This is an item important to keep in mind as sometimes, if we are not careful, it might seem that the industrious man began to make silver almost as soon as he was born, so anxious are we to give him the credit of working as early as possible. These men were jewellers and watchmakers as well as silversmiths. Others were skilled "hair workers," an art that, I venture to say, is no more.

We must not forget that our silver is getting older each year. It frequently changes hands, and records of its early existence and by whom owned are important and enhance its value.

It was Mrs. John Madison Taylor who originally suggested the publication of this book. To her must go the credit of giving it the title, "Three Centuries of Historic Silver."

The silver exhibited in the Rooms of the Pennsylvania Society of the Colonial Dames of America in 1929 and 1937 is listed, with a few additions. There are a number of silversmiths' marks included with the photographs.

The Committee wishes to thank Mr. Harrold E. Gillingham and Mr. J. Hall Pleasants for their helpful co-operation. They wish also to express their appreciation to Mr. Stephen C. G. Ensko for permission to quote from his "American Silversmiths and Their Marks," published in 1927, in writing the lives of some of the craftsmen. We are also indebted to Boston Museum of Fine Arts, The Yale University, Gallery of Fine Arts and the Metropolitan Museum for their help.

PHOEBE P. PRIME, Chairman

September 15, 1938.

LIST OF LENDERS AND OWNERS

Mrs. John Seaman Albert
Mrs. Francis O. Allen
The Misses Ashbridge
Miss Elizabeth A. Atkinson
Miss Gertrude Atkinson
Miss Caroline D. Bache
Miss Edith M. Bache
Miss Emily Hinds Bache
Mr. Franklin Bache
Mrs. Edgar Wright Baird
Mrs. John Hampton Barnes
Mrs. J. Herman Barnsley
Mrs. North Emery Bartlett
Mrs. Gibson Bell
Mrs. Henry A. Berwind, Jr.
Mrs. David Paul Brown
Mrs. T. Wistar Brown
Mr. Walter James Steele Buck
Mrs. Henry Paul Busch
Mrs. Logan M. Bullitt
Mrs. Howard Butcher, Jr.
Mrs. Francis von A. Cabeen
Mrs. James A. G. Campbell
*Mrs. Hampton L. Carson
Mr. Joseph Carson
Mrs. Henry Chapman
Mrs. Edwin M. Chance
Miss Clarissa T. Chase
Mrs. Samuel Hart Chase
Miss Xenia Clampitt
*Mrs. Edward Walter Clark
Mr. Sidney P. Clark
Mrs. W. Goodell Clark
Mrs. William J. Clothier
Dr. George Morrison Coates
Mrs. William H. Collins
Mrs. William Wistar Comfort
Mrs. Charles Conrad
*Mrs. James de W. Cookman
Mr. Rodney P. Cookman

Mrs. Andrew Wright Crawford
Mrs. Ninian C. Cregar
*Mrs. Elisha Crowell
Miss Frances Kimball Crowell
Mrs. William W. Doughten
Mrs. Edward S. Dillon
Captain Harry C. Drayton
Mrs. Russell Duane
Mr. & Mrs. M. Stevenson Easby
Mrs. Thomas Biddle Ellis
Mrs. Henry Erdman
Miss Essyllt Evans
Miss Mary Evans
Mrs. Thomas Evans
Mr. & Mrs. Christian Febiger
Mr. & Mrs. Mantle Fielding
Mrs. Charles A. Fife
Mrs. George D. Fowle
Mrs. Frederick Fraley
Mrs. William S. Freeman
Friends Historical Society
Mr. Edward Carey Gardiner
Mrs. John Marshall Gest
Mrs. Henry P. Glendinning
Mr. & Mrs. Harrold E. Gillingham
Mrs. Charles L. Glover
Mrs. W. Clarke Grieb
Mrs. Frank B. Gummey
Mr. & Mrs. William P. Hacker
*Miss Laura Curtis Haines
Mrs. Clarence F. Hand
Mrs. Meredith Hanna
Mr. W. Clarke Hanna
Mrs. H. Norris Harrison
Mr. & Mrs. John Harrison, Jr.
Mrs. Joseph Harrison
Mrs. Wm. K. Hartzell
Mrs. Joseph Linden Heacock
Mr. Samuel J. Henderson
Mr. Barry H. Hepburn

9

LIST OF LENDERS AND OWNERS—*Continued*

Mrs. Addinell Hewson
The Historical Society of
   Pennsylvania
Miss Sarah Bache Hodge
Mrs. Benjamin R. Hoffman
*Miss Anna H. Howell
Mrs. Arthur Howell
Mr. J. Robeson Howell
Mr. Lardner Howell
Miss Martha Paul Howell
Mrs. Roy Arthur Hunt
The Misses Huston
Mrs. Joseph B. Hutchinson
Miss Anna Warren Ingersoll
Mrs. Charles E. Ingersoll
Mr. & Mrs. C. Jared Ingersoll
Mrs. Albert Atlee Jackson
Mrs. Walter M. Jeffords
Mrs. William Norton Johnson
Mr. Philip Syng Justice
*Mrs. Arthur H. Lea
Mrs. Charles M. Lea
*Miss Elizabeth L. Lea
Mrs. Henry Carvill Lewis
Mrs. Drummond W. Little
*Mrs. A. Sidney Logan
Mr. Robert R. Logan
Mrs. George T. Lukens
Mrs. W. Logan MacCoy
*Mrs. Campbell Madeira
Mrs. George M. Marshall
Mrs. Charles Price Maule
Mrs. R. Wilson McCready
Mrs. Walter McInnes
Miss Augusta McMillan
Mrs. B. Franklin Mechling
Mrs. Richard Waln Meirs
Mrs. Samuel Vaughan Merrick
Mrs. Morris Hill Merritt
Dr. James Alan Montgomery
Mrs. Walter T. Moore
Miss Sarah Agnes Morison
Mr. Lawrence J. Morris
Mrs. Roland S. Morris
Mrs. Charles C. Norris, Jr.

Mrs. Thornton Oakley
Miss Ella Parsons
Miss Eleanor C. Patterson
*Mrs. Henry D. Paxson
Mrs. Charles C. Perkins
Mrs. Henry Pemberton, Jr.
Mrs. James De Wolf Perry
The Philadelphia Museum of Art
Mrs. William R. Philler
Mrs. George Plumly
The Presbyterian Historical Society
Mrs. Alfred Coxe Prime
Miss Alice M. Prime
Mrs. David Chandler Prince
Mrs. Evan Randolph
Mrs. B. Brannan Reath, 2nd
Mrs. Theodore W. Reath
Miss Ida Elizabeth Rhoad
Miss Mary Leiper Rhoad
Miss Lydia Wistar Rhoads
Mrs. William Gibbons Rhoads
Mrs. Samuel D. Risley
Miss Emilie M. Rivinus
Mr. E. Florens Rivinus
Mr. & Mrs. David Buzby Robb
Mrs. Henry B. Robb
Mrs. Louis Barclay Robinson
*Mrs. Charles F. Russell
Mrs. Winthrop Sargent
Mrs. Edwin Schenck
Mrs. Joseph W. Shannon
Mrs. Joseph W. Sharp, Jr.
Mrs. Charles D. Shellenberger
Mr. & Mrs. Daniel M. Shewbrooks
Mrs. Walter Penn Shipley
Mrs. Raymond S. Shortlidge
Mrs. Edward Wanton Smith
*Miss Louise Snowden
Mrs. Boyd Lee Spahr
Mrs. Murray H. Spahr, Jr.
Mrs. Paul Spencer
Dr. Isaac Starr
Mrs. William Hill Steeble
Mrs. Alfred Stengel
Mr. & Mrs. Arnold Gindrat Talbot

LIST OF LENDERS AND OWNERS—*Continued*

Miss Frances Katharine Talbot
Mrs. Richard P. Tatum
Mrs. J. Madison Taylor
Mr. Roland L. Taylor
Mrs. Samuel Hinds Thomas
Miss Lydia Fisher Warner
*Mrs. John M. Whitall
Mrs. Roland B. Whitridge
Mrs. Carroll Williams
Mr. & Mrs. Stanley Eyre Wilson
Mrs. Charles M. Wistar

*Mr. Daniel Wister
Miss Frances A. Wister
Mrs. James W. Wister
Mrs. William Rotch Wister
Family of the Late William Rotch
    Wister
Miss Wister
Mrs. Horatio Curtis Wood
Miss Susanna Wright
The Misses Wright

* Deceased.

PHILADELPHIA SILVERSMITHS

Anthony, Joseph, Jr.
Armstrong, Allen
Armstrong, John
Bailey & Kitchen
Ball, William
Bard, Conrad
Bartram, William
Bayley, J.
Boudinot, Elias
Britton, Jacob
Browne, Liberty
Browne & Seale
Byrne, James
Chaudron & Rasch
Chevalier, Clement E.
David, John
David, Peter
Dorsey, Joshua
Du Bois, Abraham
Dumoutet, John B., Sr.
Dupuy, Daniel
Erwin, Henry
Ferguson & Moore
Ferguson, John
Fletcher, Thomas
Fletcher & Gardiner
Foster, Abraham
Garrett, Philip
Germon, John

Ghiselin, William
Hall, David
Hollingshead, William
Howell, James
Humphreys, Richard
Jenkins, John
Leacock, John
Letelier, John
Lewis, Harvey
Lewis & Smith
Lownes, Edward
Lownes, Joseph
Maysenhoelder, Charles
McMullin, John
Milne, Edmund
Moore & Ferguson
Murdoch, John
Musgrave, James
Myers, John
Nys, Johannis
Owen, Jesse
Pancoast, Samuel
Parry & Musgrave
Pepper, Henry I.
Rasch, Anthony
Richards, Samuel, Jr.
Richards & Williamson
Richardson, Francis
Richardson, Francis, II

RICHARDSON, JOSEPH, SR.
RICHARDSON, JOSEPH, II
RICHARDSON, JOSEPH & NATHANIEL
SHIELDS, THOMAS
SHIVING, GODFREY
SHOEMAKER, JOSEPH
SIMMONS, ANTHONY
SWAN, ROBERT
SYNG, PHILIP, I
SYNG, PHILIP, II

TANGUY, JOHN
VAN VOORHIS, DANIEL
VILANT, WILLIAM
WARD, JOHN
WATSON, JAMES
WEAVER, EMMOR T.
WHARTENBY & BUMM
WILLIAMSON, SAMUEL
WILSON, R. & W.
WILTBERGER, CHRISTIAN

LANCASTER, PENNSYLVANIA
PETER GETZ

WEST CHESTER, PENNSYLVANIA
JOSHUA WEAVER

BOSTON AND NEW ENGLAND

BRADLEY, PHINEAS, New Haven, Conn.
BRIGDEN, ZACHARIAH, Boston
BURT, WILLIAM, Boston
CLEVELAND & POST, Norwich, Conn.
COWELL, WILLIAM, Boston
DODGE, NEHEMIAH, Providence, R. I.
DODGE, SERIL, Providence, R. I.
DROWNE, SAMUEL, Portsmouth, N. H.
EDWARDS, SAMUEL, Boston
EMERY, STEPHEN, Boston
HAMLIN, WILLIAM, Middletown, Conn.
HARDING, N. & Co., Boston
HOLMES, WILLIAM, Boston
HURD, JACOB, Boston
KIERSTEADE, CORNELIUS, New Haven,
  Conn.
LAKEMAN, E. K., Salem, Mass.

LORING, JOSEPH, Boston
NICHOLAS, WILLIAM S., Boston
NICHOLS, BASSETT, Boston
OLIVER, PETER, Boston
OTIS, JONATHAN, Newport, R. I.
PITKIN, WILLIAM L., E. Hartford, Conn.
REVERE, PAUL, Boston
RIDGEWAY, JAMES, Boston
ROGERS, DANIEL, Newport, R. I.
STODDER & FROBISHER, Boston
TISDALE, B. H., Boston
VERNON, SAMUEL, Newport, R. I.
WAITE, JOHN, Kingston, R. I.
WARD & BARTHOLOMEW, Hartford, Conn.
WATSON, EDWARD, Boston
WELLES, A. G., Boston
WINSLOW, EDWARD, Boston

WILMINGTON, BALTIMORE, ANNAPOLIS, AND CHARLESTON

AIKEN, GEORGE, Baltimore
BARRY, STANDISH, Baltimore
BROWNE & HOULTON, Baltimore
EWAN, JOHN, Charleston, S. C.
FARIS, WILLIAM, Annapolis, Md.
HOLLAND, LITTLETON, Baltimore
KIRK, SAMUEL, Baltimore

LYNCH, JOHN, Baltimore
RICE, JOSEPH, Baltimore
RIGGS, GEORGE W., Baltimore
STOW, JOHN, Wilmington, Del.
WARNER, THOS. & ANDREW E., Balti-
  more
WOODCOCK, BANCROFT, Wilmington, Del.

NEW YORK (CITY) AND NEW JERSEY

BANCKER, ADRIAN
BOGERT, NICHOLAS
BRASHER, EPHRAIM

BURGER, JOHN
CHITRY, PETER
COLEMAN, NATHANIEL, Burlington, N. J.

Eoff, Garret

Forbes, John W.

Forbes, William G.

Gale, William & Son

Goelet, Philip

Gough, James

Hamersley, Thomas

Hastier, Marguerite

Heyer, William B.

Hutton, Isaac, Albany, N. Y.

Lupp, Peter, New Brunswick, N. J.

Le Roux, Charles

Myers, Myer

Pearson, John

Sayre, Joel

Targee, John & Peter

Thompson, William

Van der Spiegel, Jacobus

Vernon, John

Wenman, B.

GEORGE AIKEN—Baltimore

b. 1765 d. 1832   working dates 1787–c. 1823

From the Maryland Gazette or Baltimore General Advertiser.—March 2, 1787.—"George Aiken, Goldsmith and Jeweller, In Calvert-Street, the second Door from Market Street, in the House lately occupied by Mr. Andrew Aitken, Apothecary, Begs leave to acquaint the Ladies and Gentlemen of Baltimore and the public in general, that he carries on the Goldsmith and Jewellery Business in their various branches; and also executes all manner of Devices, worked in Hair for Lockets, Rings, Pins, &c."

Mr. J. Hall Pleasants in his "Maryland Silversmiths" tells us that "Aiken was located at 1 South Calvert street from 1796 until 1801, either in the shop he had in 1787, or next door. From 1802 until 1812 he was at 72 Baltimore Street.

Pieces made by Aiken are excellent, both in design and workmanship. Judging from the quantity of Aiken silver which is still to be seen the output of his shop up to 1810 must have been quite large. He used at least seven different marks."

TEASPOONS, lent by Mr. and Mrs. C. Jared Ingersoll.
CANDLESTICKS, PAIR, lent by Mr. Joseph Carson.

JOSEPH ANTHONY, Jr.—Philadelphia

b. Rhode Island 1762 d. 1814   working dates 1783–1809

Joseph Anthony advertises, October 4th, 1783, as living in Market street two doors east of the Indian King. He

"Begs leave to inform the Public in general, and his Friends in particular, that he carries on the Gold and SilverSmith Business, in all its various branches, where he makes all kinds of work in the most elegant manner."—Follows a long list of articles from which I quote:—"Tankards, sugar dishes, cream pots, silver corkscrews, inlaid toothpick cases, Boatswains calls."—Pennsylvania Journal.

Mr. Anthony imported a great variety of articles from England, not only silver, plated ware and jewellery, but he mentions "A few setts of chimney pieces of Derbyshire petrefaction, very elegant."

For a number of years he lived at No. 94 High street.

Miss Helen Burr Smith, great, great, great granddaughter of Joseph Anthony, in an article published recently in the New York Sun tells us that "he was a first cousin of Gilbert Stuart, Elizabeth Anthony, his father's sister having married the celebrated portrait painter."

In the Metropolitan Museum in New York there is a beautiful portrait of Joseph Anthony painted by Gilbert Stuart.   Miss Smith tells us that for years this was not properly identified.   It was known as "Judge Anthony." It is considered one of the finest examples of Gilbert Stuart's work.

SOUP SPOONS, two, engraved E.H.C., lent by Mrs. Henry
 D. Paxson, deceased.

TEASPOON, engraved C.B., lent by Mrs. Henry D. Paxson,
 deceased.

CREAMER, lent by Miss Clarissa T. Chase, belonged to
 Hester Stork, great, great, great maternal grandmother
 of Miss Chase.

CANS, pair, lent by Mr. Barry Hepburn, formerly property
 of Commodore John Barry, Commodore of the American Navy.

PAP SPOON, lent by Mrs. Roland S. Morris who says that "it was used in Mr. Morris' side of the family for over a hundred years. It has the Lloyd coat of arms on it and was brought into the Morris family by a Lloyd lady who married a Morris."

ALLEN ARMSTRONG—Philadelphia

worked 1806–1817

Listed in Philadelphia Directories as "Goldsmith and Jeweller," at 225 Arch street in 1817.

TABLESPOONS and two TEASPOONS, both marked C.S., lent by Mr. and Mrs. Arnold Gindrat Talbot. They belonged to Catherine Streeper who married James Monaghan 1811; their son, Robert Emmet, married Rebecca Darlington Smith 1866; their daughter, Katherine Streeper, married Arnold Gindrat Talbot 1901.

TABLESPOONS, lent by Mrs. John Marshall Gest, engraved J.N.F.G. for John and Nancy Ferguson Greer—third cousins of Mrs. Gest.

JOHN ARMSTRONG—Philadelphia

worked 1810–1813

He worked at 5 North 2nd Street.

SIX PIECE TEA SET, lent by Mrs. Charles C. Norris, Jr., who says that they belonged to "great grandfather John Norris—about 1800 and used at many important functions."

I. BAILEY, also J. BAYLY—New York & Philadelphia
working dates 1762, 1785

Bailey worked in New York in 1762 as a silversmith and swordmaker. He is listed later in Philadelphia in 1785, as goldsmith in Cherry Alley below 3rd and Race streets.

Teaspoon, lent by Mrs. Henry D. Paxson, deceased.
*Ladle, owned by Miss Lydia Fisher Warner. This piece has the marks used by Mr. Bailey when he was working in New York. It is engraved "J.S.W.—1782," for John and Sarah Warner.

BAILEY AND KITCHEN—Philadelphia
working dates 1833–46

They are listed in the Philadelphia Directories as working at 136 Chesnut street. "Chesnut" was spelled without the "t" for many years. This firm made many large silver services which were prized wedding presents of our grandmother's day. The coffee pots often held a quart or possibly two.

Sugar Tongs, lent by Mrs. Henry D. Paxson, deceased.
Teaspoon, lent by Mrs. Henry D. Paxson, deceased, Engraved "C.B."

WILLIAM BALL—Philadelphia
b. October 26, 1729 d. May 31, 1810   working dates
1759–82

In the Pennsylvania Journal for November 13, 1766, he advertises as follows: "William Ball, has removed to Front

* An asterisk preceding an entry indicates that the item is illustrated.

street the very next door to the London Coffee house, where he continues his business of manufacturing gold and silver in all its branches, as in London, with good allowance for chapman to sell again."

He offers for sale a "commodious country house, garden and stables, suitable for a genteel family, is a healthy place and remarkable fine prospect." This property was evidently his country place, Hope Manor, which he describes in another advertisement as "adjoining Kensington."

Again we find him advertising as follows: "Ran away from the subscriber in the city of Philadelphia, and went to the British Army three negro men, viz, Tom, by trade a silversmith, about 36 years of age." Pennsylvania Packet, September 1, 1778.

In 1765 he was, with a large group of prominent Philadelphia citizens, a signer of the Non-Importation Agreement. He was the 16th member of the Schuylkill Fishing Company.

William Ball led the Goldsmiths, Silversmiths and Jewellers division in the Grand Federal Procession held in Philadelphia, July 4th, 1788, to celebrate the Ratification of the Constitution.

TABLESPOONS, pair, lent by Miss Sarah Agnes Morison. They belonged to Mary Cocke Morison, her great grandmother.

*CREAMER, owned by Mrs. Charles Perkins.

ADRIAN BANCKER—New York

b. 1703 d. 1772   working dates c. 1731–61

Adrian Bancker was the son of Evertt Bancker, Mayor of Albany. He served an apprenticeship with Hendrick

Boelen, goldsmith.   He was admitted freeman to the city in 1731 and served as collector of the South Ward 1733–36.

MUG—type sometimes called pint can—lent by Mrs. William Gibbons Rhoads.   It belonged to Mr. Rhoads and came down from his great, great grandfather, Aquilla Jones, born 1724 and died 1800.

*TANKARD, lent by Mrs. Harrold E. Gillingham. Presented to John and Ann (Jacobs) Gillingham, married, 1735.   It bears the cypher J.A.G.   The history has been written in the magazine Antiques for June, 1931.   It was exhibited in the Metropolitan Museum, December, 1931–January, 1932.

TEASPOON, lent by Mrs Harrold E. Gillingham.

CONRAD BARD—Philadelphia

working dates 1825, 1850

Worked at 80 Locust street in 1825.

LADLE, lent by Mrs. Charles Price Maule.   It belonged to Oliver and Rachel Randolph Parry.

STANDISH BARRY—Baltimore

b. 1763 d. 1844   working dates 1784–1810

"Standish Barry was the son of Lavallin Barry, a young Irishman from Dublin who settled in Baltimore before the Revolution. He was an apprentice of David Evans, a Baltimore watch and clock maker and silversmith.   Barry was frequently listed as a watch and clock maker, and later as a silversmith.   His working period covered about 25 years, and most of his pieces were made prior to 1800.   He was a member of the Baltimore Militia during the latter part of the Revolution. He saw service under Washington in the suppression of the Whiskey Rebellion in 1794. In 1812 he took part in the Battles of Bladensburg and North Point, and on more than one occasion it is said that his horse was shot from under him." This account is quoted from "Maryland Silversmiths" by J. Hall Pleasants.

*Tea Pot, owned by Mrs. M. Stevenson Easby who says the original owner was Elizabeth Poultney, daughter of Thomas and Anne Poultney, of Baltimore. She married James Large of Philadelphia on January 15, 1817.

WILLIAM BARTRAM—Philadelphia

working 1769

He advertises in the Pennsylvania Chronicle for June 19, 1769, as follows: "William Bartram, Goldsmith and Jeweler. Hath opened shop at the sign of the golden cup and crown in Front-street, exactly opposite the house of Joseph Turner, Esq., where he intends to carry on his business in all its branches, and has ready for sale, a large and neat assortment of fashionable jewelery, and elegant plate, which he will sell at the most reasonable prices.—Said Bartram makes all kinds of jewelery and Goldsmith's work, agreeable to the newest and most fashionable patterns, on the shortest notice; he also mends all sorts of jewelery, gold or silver work, in the neatest manner, and gives the highest price for old gold and silver."

*Salver, lent by Mrs. Alfred C. Prime. As she is editing this book, she takes this piece of silver as an example of many incorrectly engraved articles which often lead the unwary student, and others, astray. Only recently, did she endeavour to untangle the mystery of this piece with most unsatisfactory results. The tray is marked with four series of initials. The first, "J.P." 1733. She found that the J.P. in question was not born until 1739. Follows, "W.P." with dates. "C.S.P.," more dates, and "W.B.P.," also with dates. On looking over her family records she finds that none of these gentlemen were either born, married, or died on the dates mentioned.

Beware of any dates on family silver, especially if they seem to indicate being engraved at a later period than when the piece was made!

*SALT CELLARS, pair, lent by Mrs. Alfred Coxe Prime. These are marked underneath "John and Rebecca Phillips." They were left by a distant cousin to the present owner and their history is as follows: John Phillips married Rebecca Pyewell, April 10, 1766; their son, William Phillips, married Anna Smith, April 29, 1799; their son, Clements Stocker Phillips, married Mary Brinton, October 25, 1838; their son, Clement Stocker Phillips, married Anna Clifford Biddle, November 15, 1881, and their daughter now owns them.

NICHOLAS BOGERT—New York

Bogert worked at 10 Lombard street in 1801.

SUGAR BOWL, lent by Mr. and Mrs. Arnold Gindrat Talbot. It belonged to Amey Martin who married Samuel Richmond in 1806. Their daughter, Charlotte, married Charles Nicholl Talbot in 1833. Their son, William Richmond, married Mary Cornelia Arnold in 1861. Their son, Arnold Gindrat, married Katherine Streeper Monaghan in 1901.

Tea Pot, lent by Mrs. Charles D. Shellenberger. It was used by her great grandmother in Portland, Maine, during the war of 1812 and lent by her grandmother to General Sherman for a Christmas party he gave his officers in Savannah, Georgia, in 1864.

ELIAS BOUDINOT

b. 1706 d. 1770   working date 1747

The Pennsylvania Journal for September 10, 1747, announces that Elias Boudinot "Is removed from Market Street to the House where Joseph Noble lately lived, in Second-street near to Black Horse Alley."

*Tankard, lent by Mr. E. Florens Rivinus. Inherited by the present owner from his great, great grandmother, Mary Stevenson, who was reliably reported by family tradition as having received it from Benjamin Franklin.

PHINEAS BRADLEY—New Haven, Conn.

1745–97

George Munson Curtis says: "His house and shop were located in Crown street. He served in the Revolution and was Captain of a company of New Haven men. At the British invasion of New Haven, July, 1779, he did valiant service with his men at the bridge on the road leading to Milford."

Soup Ladle, lent by Mr. & Mrs. Rodney P. Cookman.

EPHRAIM BRASHER—New York

worked c. 1786–1805

Member of the Gold and Silver Smiths Society, 1786.

Employed by the United States Mint to make assays on some gold and silver coins in 1792. Minted the famous "Brasher Dubloon." Assistant Justice to the City in 1796.

LADLE, lent by Mrs. Louis Barclay Robinson. It was inherited from her grandmother whose maiden name was Lounds.

ZACHARIAH BRIGDEN—Boston

1734–1787

Shop located on Corn Hill.

THREE-LEGGED CREAMER, lent by Mrs. Charles L. Glover who says: "The creamer was owned by John Cotton (1712–1789) who was fourth in line from the famous John Cotton, Boston, 1633. It descended to me lineally through the succeeding five generations."

JACOB BRITTIN or BRITTON—Philadelphia

working date 1807

Working at 45 North 2nd street in 1807.

TABLE SPOONS, lent by Mrs. John Marshall Gest. Engraved J.F.R. for Captain James Francis (Grier) Ralston, the great grandfather of Mrs. Gest. He served in the War of 1812.

LIBERTY BROWNE—Philadelphia

working 1801–19

Listed as Jeweller 70 south Front st. in Directories. Of the firm of Browne and Seale.

SUGAR BOWL, CREAMER, and WASTE BOWL, lent by Miss Eleanor C. Patterson who says: "My great grandmother told my father they were ordered for her wedding in May, 1800, by her father, Colonel Christopher Stuart, a young Irishman who came over here and fought with Washington. Christopher Stuart arrived in America, 1770. He became Captain 5th Pennsylvania Battalion, 1776; Major in the Battalion, same year; Major 5th Pennsylvania Line, 1777; and Lieutenant Colonel 3rd Pennsylvania Line, 1780. He was taken prisoner at the capture of Fort Washington and exchanged in 1777. He also engaged in the battles of Long Island and Monmouth. His daughter, Martha Bull Stuart, who received the silver, married John Patterson in 1800. The silver has been in daily use since then."

TABLESPOONS, pair, lent by Mrs. Clarence F. Hand. Marked M.L. for Mary Laycock, who was born in Darby, February 25, 1786.

BROWNE AND HOULTON—Baltimore

working date 1799

Mr. J. Hall Pleasants in his "Maryland Silversmiths" says: "Browne & Houlton, goldsmiths, had their shop at 123 Baltimore Street in 1799. There is no question that the last named partner was John Houlton, the silversmith and engraver, who had a shop at 122 Baltimore Street in 1800 and who had previously had a shop in Philadelphia from 1794–98. No silver by Brown & Houlton has been seen."

*CREAMER, lent by Mrs. Evan Randolph. The mark on this piece as well as the piece itself has been reproduced

in this book.   Mrs. Randolph tells us that "it has initials
W.M.B. in bowknot and wheat ear design.   It was inherited by Robert Bethell, whose daughters gave it to
their cousin, Anne Lee Carson, who gave it to her daughter, the present owner.   Height 3 3/4 inches at lip.
Width at top 2 3/8 inches.   Beaded edge.   Rectangular
bottom with concave flutings."

BROWNE AND SEALE—Philadelphia
working dates 1810–11

Liberty Browne and William Seale are listed in the Philadelphia Directory of 1811 as jewellers at 119 Chesnut
Street.

CHILD's MUG or CAN, lent by Mrs. Evan Randolph.   The
initials on it are "R.B." for Robert Bethell.   It has a
scroll handle and bands of incised lines on the sides.
PITCHER, lent by Mrs. Charles C. Norris, Jr.   It belonged
to her grandfather, John Norris, about 1800.
*BEAKER, lent by Mrs. Alfred C. Prime.   Belonged to her
grandfather, John Barclay Biddle (b. 1815 d. 1879),
whose daughter Anna Clifford Biddle married Clement
S. Phillips (b. 1851 d. 1915).
TEA POTS, two, lent by Mrs. Samuel Hinds Thomas.   The
silver teapots belonged to her great uncle, Commodore
James Biddle, who used them on his ship while Commander of the Pacific Fleet.

JOHN BURGER—New York
working dates 1786–1807

John Burger was a member of the Gold and Silver

Smiths Society, 1786. He worked at 153 Water Street where he solicited orders for large plate, at 207 Queen Street in 1789 and at 62 James Street in 1779–1807.

LARGE SPOONS, two, lent by Mrs. Harrold E. Gillingham.

WILLIAM BURT—Boston

1726–52   working date 1747

*PORRINGER lent by Mrs. Harrold E. Gillingham.

JAMES BYRNE—Philadelphia

working dates 1784–85

This silversmith advertises in the Penna. Packet of October 18, 1784: "James Byrne Begs leave to inform his friends and the public that he has removed from opposite the city Tavern, Second-street, to Front street, three doors above Chesnut street; where he continues to carry on the different branches of the jewellery, gold smith's and plated-ware business; He has at present an elegant Assortment of Goods of the first quality in that line, which he is determined to sell on the most reasonable terms."

TABLESPOON, lent by Mr. and Mrs. Arnold Gindrat Talbot. It is marked C. It was owned by Barbara Clark who married Abram Gindrat in 1803. Their daughter, Louisa Caroline, married Richard James Arnold in 1825. Their daughter, Mary Cornelia Arnold, married William Richmond Talbot in 1861. Their son, Arnold Gindrat Talbot, married Katherine Streeper Monaghan in 1901.

T. BYRNES—an unlisted silversmith
TEAPOT, lent by Dr. Isaac Starr.

CHAUDRON & RASCH—Philadelphia
working date c. 1812
At the time of George Washington's burial Chaudron
delivered the funeral oration at the French Lodge de Am-
enité.   They held "Open Lodge" that day.

*LARGE COFFEE URN, lent by Mrs. Charles Price Maule.
Original owner, Sarah Syng Physic Randolph.
*COFFEE POT and *TEA POT, lent by Mrs. W. Clarke
Grieb.   See family history under Joel Sayre.

CLEMENT E. CHEVALIER—Philadelphia
working dates 1816–18, 23, 33
SILVER PITCHER, lent by Mrs. Murray H. Spahr.   Presented to her great, great grandfather, Anthony Cuth-
bert, Engineer, for services in connection with the
opening of the High Street Bridge.

PETER CHITRY—New York
working dates 1814–25
He worked in Burrows and Henry streets, 1820.

*CREAMER, lent by Mrs. John Madison Taylor.   Brought
from Charleston, South Carolina, by Colonel William
Drayton about 1814.

CLEVELAND & POST—Norwich, Connecticut
working date 1816
NURSING NIPPLE, lent by Mrs. Harrold E. Gillingham.

NATHANIEL COLEMAN—Burlington, New Jersey
b. 1765 d. 1842   working date c. 1790 on

His shop at No. 320 High street in Burlington is supposed to be still standing.   He was a Quaker.

TABLESPOON, lent by Mrs. Thomas Biddle Ellis.

CREAMER, lent by Mrs. David B. Robb who says "It belonged to Sarah Burr, daughter of Hudson Burr, born, 1776.   She married in 1796 William Woolman of Burlington, New Jersey (born 1765–died 1854).   He was a member of New Jersey General Assembly, 1821–23 and Manager of Burlington Library Company which was chartered in 1757 by King George II."

WILLIAM COWELL—Boston
b. 1682 d. 1736

SUGAR TONGS, lent by Miss Hannah C. Wright and Miss Margaret E. Wright.

JOHN DAVID, son of PETER—Philadelphia
d. 1794   working dates 1763–77

In The Pennsylvania Gazette for January 13, 1763, he advertises the following: "John David, Goldsmith, Having opened Shop next door to Second-street corner, in Chesnut-street.   Makes and sells all manner of Gold and Silver Work, in the neatest Manner.   Those who are pleased to favour him with their Custom, may depend on being faithfully served, and at the most reasonable Rates.   N.B. He also gives the full Value for old Gold and Silver."   In the Pennsylvania Gazette for March, 1765, we find that he "is removed from Chesnut into Second-street, where he carries on the Goldsmith's Business as usual."

TEA SERVICE, four pieces, lent by Miss Caroline D. Bache, who says the silver came from the Meade side of the family. Mrs. Hartman Bache was General George Gordon Meade's sister and Miss Bache's grandmother.

*BOWL and CREAMER, lent by Miss Louise Snowden, deceased. Now the property of the Philadelphia Museum of Art. Engraved "N.S.S." for Reverend Nathaniel Randolph and Sarah Snowden who were married in 1792.

*CREAMER, owned by Miss Lydia Fisher Warner. This creamer is inverted pear shape with a splay base, gadrooned edge, and double curved handle.

*SUGAR URN, *WASTE BOWL, SOUP and *DESSERT SPOONS, lent by Mrs. Henry B. Robb. They belonged to her great, great grandfather, Nathaniel Mitchell. In 1780–81 he was Brigade Major. In 1782 he was Prisoner of War on Parole and delegate to the First Continental Congress in Delaware in 1786, 1788. He was Governor of Delaware from 1805–1808 and a member of the Delaware Society of the Cincinnati.

DESSERT SPOONS, pair, lent by Mrs. Alfred Coxe Prime. Family silver. Feather edge.

LADLES, pair, lent by Mrs. Alfred Coxe Prime.

LARGE SPOONS, two, with scroll on back of bowl, lent by Mrs. Harrold E. Gillingham.

LARGE SPOON, lent by Mrs. Hampton L. Carson, deceased.

*SUGAR BOWL, lent anonymously.

PETER DAVID—Philadelphia

d. 1755   advertised 1739

The American Weekly Mercury for April 26, 1739, states that Peter David had his shop in Front Street.

SUGAR TONGS, lent by Miss Elizabeth Allen Atkinson. They belonged to her great grandmother, Elizabeth Ackley Allen.

*TANKARD, lent by Mr. and Mrs. David Buzby Robb. This piece belonged to William Hudson, third Mayor of Philadelphia in 1725–26. He was also Member of City Council and Alderman. He was born, 1662, and died in 1742.

William Hudson married Mary Richardson. Samuel Hudson married Mary Holton. Susanna Hudson married John Burr who was surveyor general for the Proprietors of West Jersey. Hudson Burr married Phebe Lippincott. Sarah Burr married William Woolman. Elizabeth Haines married Thomas Burr Woolman. Thomas Robb married Caroline E. Woolman. Walter E. Robb married Ella C. Buzby and David B. Robb married Sarah Whelen Carson.

William Hudson married in 1688 Mary, daughter of Samuel Richardson, who was the Provisional Councillor, and a Justice.

Thomas Allen Glenn has described the house of the William Hudson's in the following clear fashion:

"It stood on a large lot of ground facing the Southeast corner of Third and Chestnut streets. It was built of red and black glazed brick and was three stories high, having a sloping roof. A brick portico extended from the front entrance. The house was surrounded by a paved courtyard, shut in from the street by a high wall, there being a coachway on Third street and another entrance gate on Chestnut street. The place was shaded by several old trees and a charming view of the Delaware could be obtained from the garden sloping away on the southeast towards Dock Creek. The stable and servants quarters were built in the rear of the courtyard. . . . The furniture was in keeping with the best style of the time. Black walnut was the principal wood used with an occasional oak or mahogany piece."

Somehow this interesting picture helps one to visualize this tankard in its original surroundings. Mrs. Robb says that this tankard has been handed down through nine generations of direct descent from William Hudson to David Buzby Robb.

DICKINSON AND HENRY—Philadelphia

Listed in Philadelphia Directory as "Jewellers and Hair workers 73 High street" in 1793.

SUGAR TONGS, lent by Mrs. Joseph Wellington Shannon.

NEHEMIAH DODGE—Providence, R. I.

working dates 1795–1824

Nehemiah Dodge advertises on September 24, 1795, in the United States Chronicle as follows: "Nehemiah Dodge informs the public that he hath opened a shop near the Church next door south of Dr. Throops where he makes and sells all kinds of smith's work."

SERVING SPOON, about 16 inches long, lent by Mrs. E. Walter Clark, deceased. It is now owned by her son, Mr. Sidney P. Clark.

SERIL DODGE—Providence, R. I.

b. 1765 d. 1803   working dates 1793–1803

Seril Dodge advertises as follows: "At his new shop opposite the Market, lately occupied by Messieurs Hopkins and Snow, offers a great variety of gold smith's and jewellery work.   At the Sign of the Arm and Gold Ear-Ring."
—United States Chronicle for February 21, 1793.

SPOON, lent by Mr. and Mrs. Arnold Gindrat Talbot.   It belonged to Gustavus Taylor in 1790 of Providence, Rhode Island.

JOSHUA DORSEY—Philadelphia

working dates 1796–1804

Joshua Dorsey is described in the Federal Gazette of October 24, 1796, as "Goldsmith, jeweller, and hair-worker, at No. 44 Market street."   On September 29, 1800, the Pennsylvania Packet states: "Joshua Dorsey, Gold and Silversmith, Has removed from No. 44, Market street, to No. 113, north Second street, opposite Lesher's tavern, where he continues the above business in all its branches, and solicits the patronage of his friends."

TALL SUGAR BOWL WITH LID, lent by Mrs. William Norton Johnson.

SAMUEL DROWNE—Portsmouth, New Hampshire

b. 1749 d. 1815

TABLESPOON, lent by Mrs. Alfred C. Prime.   Bought from sale of Mrs. Miles White, Jr.   Feather edge.   Engraved W.E.W. with a shell on back of bowl.

ABRAHAM DUBOIS—Philadelphia

d. 1807   working dates 1777–1802

The Pennsylvania Evening Post for May 20, 1777, announces the following: "Abraham Dubois has for sale at his house in Second street, four doors below Arch street, . . . some very neat gold and silver watches, neat gold lockets, and different kinds of silver work and jewellery."

*LARGE TEAPOT and *SUGAR URN, with gallery, lent by Mr. and Mrs. Christian Febiger. These pieces belonged to Christian Febiger. See history under Joseph Lownes.

CHALICES, pair, lent by the Presbyterian Historical Society. They were a gift to the First Presbyterian Church in Amwell, New Jersey, and are inscribed as follows: "A gift of the Hon'rble John Reading, Esqr, Deceas'd, in Amwell, 1767." These chalices are very plain with bell-shaped bodies, supported on stems with compressed knops and moulded bases. The maker's mark stamped on them is "AD." This may have been Abraham Dubois although he is not listed as working until ten years later. The only other "AD" recorded, is the mark of Amos Doolittle, working in Connecticut (born 1754). It is not likely that he would be putting his name on a chalice at 13 years of age. Hon. John Reading, the donor, was a member of the King's Council and Governor of New Jersey. These chalices are described in E. Alfred Jones' "Old Silver of American Churches."

JOHN BAPTISTE DUMOUTET—Philadelphia

working dates 1793–1816

Dumoutet is listed in the Philadelphia Directory as working at 71 Elm street in 1793. The (Philadelphia)

Aurora for November 26, 1799, announces the following: "John Dumoutet, Senr., Goldsmith & Jeweller, No. 193, So. Second Street. Jewellery of all kinds Finished under his immediate inspection, consisting of Ladies and Gentlemen's Gold Watch Chains, with Seals, Watchkeys, Sleeve Buttons, Stock and Knee-Buckles, Snuff Boxes, Medallions, Bracelets, Bosom-Pins, Plain and Stone Rings, Necklaces, Drops, Ear-Rings & all of Gold. Likewise An extensive variety of Ornaments too tedious to enumerate. He works Hair in the most elegant manner, according to the fancy of those who please to honor him with their commands."

SOUP SPOON, lent by Mrs. Henry D. Paxson, deceased.
SUGAR TONGS, lent anonymously.
SPOONS, lent by Mrs. George Plumly.
LARGE SPOON, lent by Mrs. Harrold E. Gillingham.

DANIEL DUPUY—Philadelphia

b. New York 1719 d. 1807   working dates 1746–1805

Daniel Dupuy was born in New York and moved to Philadelphia in 1740. He served an apprenticeship to his brother-in-law, Peter David. Later on his two sons, John and Daniel, assisted him in business. In November, 1781, the Pennsylvania Packet advertises the following: "Scales and Weights for weighing of gold; best plated spurs; and a variety of Silver work; to be sold by Daniel Dupuy, in Second-Street, next door but one to the Meeting house."

TEASPOONS, lent by Mrs. Henry D. Paxson, deceased.
CREAMER, SUGAR URN WITH GALLERY and WASTE BOWL, lent by The Misses Ashbridge. They are now in the Philadelphia Art Museum.

Sugar Tongs, lent by Mrs. Ninian Caldwell Cregar. Engraved "M.R." for Mary Roberts who was born in 1758. Belongs to her great, great, great granddaughter, Mary Rebecca Cregar.

Spoons, four, lent by Mrs. Wilson McCredy.

*Porringer, lent by Mrs. Walter T. Moore. Marked I.G.E. for John & Elizabeth Guest, Mrs. Moore's great, great grandparents.

Coffee Spoons, six, lent by Mrs. Alfred C. Prime.

SAMUEL EDWARDS—Boston

b. 1705 d. 1762   working date 1729

Samuel Edwards, son of John Edwards, silversmith, was born in Boston. He opened shop in 1729 and received commissions from the General Assembly to manufacture plate for presentation purposes.

Tablespoon, rat tail, lent by Mrs. Alfred C. Prime. Bought at the sale held by Mrs. Miles White, Jr.

STEPHEN EMERY—Boston

b. 1725 d. 1801

Stephen Emery is mentioned with Joseph Loring as a bondsman and silversmith, July 24, 1788, in the Boston Selectmen's Records.

Punch Ladle, lent by Mrs. Henry Chapman.

GARRET EOFF—New York

b. 1785 d. 1858

Eoff worked at 23 Elm Street, 1814. He was of the

firms, Eoff & Howell; Eoff & Connor; Eoff & Phyfe; Eoff & Moore.

Sugar Bowl and two Creamers, lent by Mrs. J. Madison Taylor.

HENRY ERWIN—Philadelphia

working dates 1817–1829

Worked at 26 South Third street in 1820.

Dessert Spoons, two, lent by Mrs. Charles M. Lea.
Forks, two, lent by Mrs. Charles M. Lea.

JOHN EWAN

Worked in Charleston, South Carolina, in 1800.

Pitcher, lent by Mrs. Samuel Hart Chase, owned by Susanna Middleton (1760–1834), sister of Arthur Middleton, a signer of the Declaration of Independence.

WILLIAM FARIS—Annapolis

b. London 1728 d. 1804   working dates 1760–80

Mr. J. Hall Pleasants in his "Maryland Silversmiths" tells us: "William Faris came first to Philadelphia from London, and then removed to Annapolis in 1757.   He was a watchmaker as well as a silversmith.   His diary has been found and contains an interesting picture of the life of the day in Annapolis.   His customers included most of the notable men of Annapolis.   He was a tavern keeper too, and tells us the price charges for accomodation and refreshments.

"Toward the latter part of his life he evidently found the tavern keeping more profitable than the silversmithing business, for his diary seems to indicate that he repaired watches and silver to a certain extent but did not make much plate at that time."

Mr. Pleasants continues: "Only a few pieces of hollow ware have come to light . . . Considering the long period covered by William Faris shop activities it is quite remarkable that more examples of his silver have not been found."

Mug, lent by Mrs. Theodore W. Reath.

JOHN C. FARR—Boston

working date 1812

Salt Spoon, lent by Mrs. John Seaman Albert. This spoon came from the Randolphs.

JOHN FERGUSON—Philadelphia

working dates 1803–10

Listed in Philadelphia Directories as working at 45 South Second Street in 1807–09.

Tablespoons, two, lent by Mrs. Wilson McCredy.

THOMAS FLETCHER—Philadelphia

working dates 1814–1850

Listed in the Philadelphia Directories as working for many years at 188 Chesnut street.

Large Pitcher, lent by Mr. and Mrs. Arthur Lea, deceased.

LARGE PITCHER, lent by Mrs. Charles M. Lea.

FORKS, two, lent by Mrs. H. Norris Harrison.

FORKS, four, lent by Mrs. Henry Carvill Lewis. These forks were part of the wedding silver of her great grandmother, Mrs. Nicholas Biddle.

SUGAR TONGS, lent by Mrs. Henry Carvill Lewis. The tongs are part of wedding silver of Mr. Lewis' great grandmother, Mrs. Henry Carvill.

FLETCHER AND GARDINER—Philadelphia

working dates 1812–1825

This firm advertises in the Philadelphia Directories as silversmith and jewellers, South East Corner 4th and Chesnut streets, in 1816.

SUGAR BOWL and CREAMER, lent by Mrs. Francis Olcott Allen. Belonged to Mary Elizabeth Dulles and Langdon Chevis, speaker of the House and first President of the Bank of the United States in Charleston.

COFFEE POT, SUGAR BOWL, TWO TEA POTS, WASTE BOWL and CREAMER, lent by Mr. and Mrs. Lewis Neilson. This set belonged to Mr. and Mrs. William D. Lewis, grandparents of Mr. Neilson.

CHILD'S MUG, lent by Mrs. Edgar W. Baird.

CAKE BASKET, lent by Mrs. David Paul Brown.

FISH KNIFE, lent by Mrs. T. Wistar Brown.

CAKE BASKET, TEA POT and ASPARAGUS FORK, lent by Mrs. William Rotch Wister. The tea pot and cake basket have the Gibbs crest engraved on them. All these pieces were the gift of Mary Gibbs to her daughter, Ruth, on her marriage to Rev. William Ellery Channing in 1814.

JOHN W. FORBES—New York

working dates 1802–1835

Worked at 415 Pearl Street till 1805. Appointed weigher and measurer for the Government in 1835.

CHILD'S SPOON, lent by Mrs. Harrold E. Gillingham.
SUGAR BOWL with lid, lent by Mrs. Louis Barclay Robinson. It was inherited from her grandmother whose maiden name was Lounds.

WILLIAM G. FORBES—New York

working dates 1773–1809

William G. Forbes was admitted freeman, February 3, 1773. Worked at 88 Broadway till 1789. Member of the Gold and Silversmiths Society, 1786. Located at 90 Broadway, 1805–09, with Garret Forbes.

BASIN, lent by the Presbyterian Historical Society and described as follows: "A plain silver basin of circular form, 9 3/4 inches in diameter. It belonged originally to the old Scotch Presbyterian Church of New York City, founded in 1756.
    "The basin is inscribed:
    "From the Scotch Presbyterian Church
    New York U.S.A. To Rev. J.F.
    Holcomb, Jhansi India."
The basin was presented to the Presbyterian Historical Society by the Rev J. H. Holcomb, who was for many years a missionary in India.

ABRAHAM FOSTER—Philadelphia

working date 1816

Advertised at 102 High street.

TABLESPOON, lent by Mrs. Harrold E. Gillingham.

WILLIAM GALE & SON—New York
working dates 1823–50

Located at Liberty street.

PAP BOAT, lent by Mrs. Francis Olcott Allen. Belonged to her great grandmother, Sarah Anderson.

PHILIP GARRETT—Philadelphia
working dates 1801–35

Listed as watchmaker No. 44 High street.

SALT SPOONS, pair, lent by Miss Hannah C. and Miss Margaret E. Wright.
COFFEE POT, lent by the Misses Wright.
CREAMER, lent by Mrs. Alfred Coxe Prime.

J. GASKINS
c. 1760

TEASPOONS, pair, lent by Mrs. Benjamin Hoffman.

JOHN D. GERMON or GERMAN—Philadelphia
working dates 1782–1825

Listed in the Philadelphia Directories as working at 33 & 35 North 3rd street, 1791 and at 248 South 2nd street in 1825.

*Salt Spoons, pair, lent by Mr. and Mrs. Christian Febiger. The original owners were Christian Febiger (1746–1796) and his wife, Elizabeth Carson Febiger (1754–1817). See life of Christian Febiger under Joseph Lownes.

PETER GETZ—Lancaster, Pennsylvania

working date 1790

Creamer, lent by Mrs. Alfred C. Prime.

WILLIAM GHISELIN—Philadelphia

working dates 1751–1762

Mr. J. Hall Pleasants in his "Maryland Silversmiths" says: "William Ghiselin, grandson of Cesar Ghiselin, the early Philadelphia and Annapolis silversmith, may be identical with William Ghiselin who advertises as follows:

" 'William Ghiselin, Goldsmith, is removed from his late dwelling house in Second-street to the house where the widow Bright lately lived, a little below the Church, in Second-street where he continues his business as usual.'— Penna. Gazette, November 14, 1751."

*Creamer, lent by The Philadelphia Museum of Art.
*Porringer, lent by Mrs. Walter T. Moore. Engraved T.A.C.

PHILIP GOELET—New York

b. 1701 d. 1748   working dates 1731–47

Teaspoons, two, lent by Miss Margaret E. Wright and Miss Hannah C. Wright.

JAMES GOUGH—New York

working dates 1769–1795

SUGAR TONGS, lent by Mrs. R. Wilson McCredy.

DAVID HALL—Philadelphia

working dates 1765–d. 1779

The following interesting announcement is taken from the Pennsylvania Gazette for December 19, 1765:

"At a meeting of the Heart and Hand Fire-Company, Philadelphia, Dec. 5, 1765, We the Members of said Company, taking into our serious Consideration the late unconstitutional and oppresive Stamp Act, and further consideration that John Hughes, Esq., a Member of this Company, is the Person appointed to distribute the detestable Stamps in the Province (and still continues to hold the said Commission in Contempt of the general Voice of his Country and Fellow-Citizens) have unanimously agreed, that unless Mr. Hughes do immediately resign his said odious Commission, without any Equivocation, Evasion or Mental Reservation, he shall no longer continue a Member of this Company, but be held in the utmost Contempt by each of us. . . . Signed by Order of the Company. David Hall, Goldsmith, Clerk."

The year following we read: "David Hall, In Second-street, near Chesnut-street, Philadelphia, Continues to make and sell all Sorts of gold and silver work. . . . Likewise china bowls etc. drilled and clasped and wood handles neatly fixed to china tea pots etc."—Penna. Gazette, February 20, 1766.

*COFFEE POT, lent by Mrs. John W. Pepper, deceased.

LADLE, lent by The Misses Hannah C. and Margaret E. Wright.

THOMAS HAMERSLY—New York

b. 1727 d. 1781   working date c. 1756

"Not only was he a silversmith, but a shrewd investor, putting his savings into real estate which, in the course of the development of Manhattan Island, immensely increased in value.   His descendants today are numbered among the wealthiest and socially most important families of the city. Among his patrons were churches and wealthy Knicker-bockers.   There was about his silver a dignity which endeared it to collectors."—Bulletin of the Metropolitan Museum 14 : 67.

*TANKARD, lent by Mr. Joseph Carson.

WILLIAM HAMELIN—Middletown, Connecticut

b. 1772   working date c. 1791

TABLESPOON, lent by Mrs. William Wistar Comfort.

N. HARDING & CO.—Boston

working c. 1800–50

SUGAR BOWL, lent by Mrs. William Rotch Wister. Stamped "coin" and engraved with the Channing Crest. It was the gift of Mary Gibbs to her daughter, Ruth, on her marriage to Reverend William Ellery Channing in 1814.

MARGUERITE HASTIER—New York

working date c. 1771

SPOONS, two lent, by Mrs. Harrold E. Gillingham.

WILLIAM B. HEYER—New York

working date 1798–1827

Worked at 47 Warren street until 1827. Of the firm of Heyer and Gale.

SUGAR BOWL, lent by Mrs. Samuel D. Risley. It came from her grandmother, Harriet Whitney Bradley, New Haven, Connecticut.

LITTLETON HOLLAND—Baltimore

b. circa 1770 d. 1847   working dates 1800–1847

"Littleton Holland was one of the leading silversmiths of his time and many attractive pieces, especially complete tea sets by him, are owned by old Baltimore families. He was in business in the same shop with Peter Little, the watch and clock maker, at 122 Baltimore street till 1814. . . . From 1816 to 1818 his shop was at 217 Baltimore street, and thereafter till his death in 1847 at 13 St. Paul street. Holland was a Mason. The inventory of his personal effects, principally silverware and jewellery in his shop and his household effects showed personal property valued at $1530.00."—From "Maryland Silversmiths" by Mr. J. Hall Pleasants.

CREAMER AND SUGAR BOWL, lent by Mrs. Clifford Lewis, Jr.

WILLIAM HOLLINGSHEAD—Philadelphia

working dates 1757–1785

Listed in Philadelphia Directories as "goldsmith," corner of Second and Arch streets, in 1785.

TEASPOON, lent by Mrs. Harrold E. Gillingham. It has a pheasant on bowl.

*CREAMER, lent by Mrs. William Doughten.

SUGAR BOWL, lent by Mrs. William H. Collins who says it came to her through a "Drinker" ancestor.

*CAN, owned by Miss Essyllt Evans.

WILLIAM HOLMES—Boston

b. 1717 d. 1783   working date c. 1737

Born in Boston. Married Rebecca Dawes, July 14, 1733. Mentioned as a master goldsmith in 1739. Was warden, grain purchaser and justice of the town. Captain of Artillery Company. Worked at Ann Street, 1789, 1813.

*PORRINGER, owned by the family of the late Mr. William Rotch Wister. It has a keyhole handle and is engraved I.L.R. The maker's mark is W.H., and it is attributed to William Holmes as the family history seems to substantiate this. It was made for Joseph and Love (Macy) Rotch. Love Macy was born at Nantucket, February 9th, 1713, and died at Nantucket, November 14, 1767. She was the daughter of Thomas Macy and Deborah Coffin of Nantucket. She married Joseph Rotch, son of William and Hannah Rotch, at Nantucket, February 21, 1733. Their son, William Rotch, married Elizabeth Barney. Their daughter, Elizabeth

Rotch, married Samuel Rodman, son of Thomas and Mary Borden Rodman. Their daughter, Mary Rodman, married in 1805 William Logan Fisher of "Wakefield," Bristol Township, Philadelphia County. Their daughter, Sarah Logan Fisher, married in 1826 William Wister of "Vernon," Germantown. William and Sarah Logan (Fisher) Wister were the parents of the late William Rotch Wister. His mother left the porringer to him. He married Mary R. Eustis. Their daughter, Frances A. Wister, traced this history.

JAMES HOWELL—Philadelphia

working dates 1802–1813

Listed in the 1809 Philadelphia Directory as working at 50 South Front street.

Two Tea Pots and Sugar Bowl with Lid, lent by Mrs. Gibson Bell. The pieces belonged to her great, great, great grandmother, Elizabeth Dawson, and descended directly to Mrs. Bell.

Creamer, lent by Miss Martha Paul Howell. Engraved on side M.P. to M.S.S.

Tablespoon and Two Teaspoons, lent by Miss Margaret E. and Miss Hannah C. Wright.

JAMES HOWELL & CO.—Philadelphia

working dates 1802–1809

*Coffee Pot, owned by Mrs. M. Stevenson Easby. The original owner was Rebecca Hartshorne, born June 11th, 1781, daughter of Patterson and Susanna Waln

Hartshorne. She married John Large of Philadelphia on June 10, 1806.

RICHARD HUMPHREYS—Philadelphia

working dates 1771–1796

The following three items are worthy of being quoted in full. In the Pennsylvania Gazette for November 7th, 1771, we find the following: "Just imported from London, fresh quantities of Dr. Hills American Balsam, to be sold at Wilmington, by Richard Humphreys, Goldsmith." Why, we wonder (nothing, however, to do with goldsmithing), did Dr. Hill have to import American Balsam? If he had not done so, possibly, we would not have had the date when Mr. Humphreys was working.

We next find him a widower. "On Wednesday last departed this Life in the 21st Year of her Age, greatly regretted, Mrs. Hannah Humphreys, the virtuous Consort of Mr. Richard Humphreys, of this City, Silversmith. The Day following her Remains (attended by many respectable Citizens) were deposited in Friends Burying Ground." —Penna. Gazette for February 24, 1773.

There is another advertisement of interest which appears also in the Penna. Gazette for September 23, 1772, showing that Mr. Humphreys was a friend of Mr. Philip Syng and succeeded him. "Richard Humphreys, Goldsmith. Having taken the house in which Philip Syng, lately dwelt, hereby informs his friends and the public, that he now carries on the Goldsmith's Business in all its branches at the aforesaid place, a few doors below the Coffee-house, where he has for sale, a neat and general assortment of Gold and Silver Ware . . . Richard Humphreys."

"The subscriber having lately removed into Upper Merion township, hereby informs his friends and former customers, that they may be supplied as usual, at his late dwelling, by the above named Richard Humphreys, whom he hereby recommends to them, as a person qualified to serve them on the best terms, and whose fidelity in the above business will engage their future confidence and regard.—Philip Syng."

Humphreys took John Myers, a poor boy, aged 16 years, as apprentice, January 25, 1773. John Myers advertised as goldsmith, 1785–1804.

*COFFEE POT, lent by Dr. James Alan Montgomery. This was once owned by Bishop White, Rector of Christ Church, for 65 years, from 1779 to his death in 1836. He was also Chaplain of Congress during the Revolution.

TEA POT, SUGAR BOWL, PITCHER and WASTE BOWL, lent by Mrs. John M. Whitall, deceased. They were once used at "Wyck," Germantown.

SALT CELLARS, lent by Mr. Lawrence J. Morris.

TEA CADDY or CANNISTER, lent by Mrs. Horatio Curtis Wood.

*TODDY STRAINER, lent by The Misses Hannah C. and Margaret E. Wright.

CAN, lent by Mr. Lardner Howell. It was a wedding present to Sarah Howell who married Walter Franklin in 1797. His grandson, Dr. Walter Franklin Atlee, presented the can to Lardner and Anna Thomas Howell at the time of their marriage in 1907.

*SWORD HILT, owned by Mr. Lawrence J. Morris. This sword was given to Colonel Tench Tilghman by Continental Congress, October, 1781.

*CAN, lent by Mrs. M. Stevenson Easby. Owned by Susanna Waln, daughter of Robert and Rebecca Waln, granddaughter of Nicholas Waln who came to America on the ship "Welcome" with William Penn. Susanna Waln was a sister of Robert Waln, a Representative in Congress. She married, December 10th, 1776, Patterson Hartshorne, son of Hugh and Hannah Hartshorne of the Borough of Bristol, Bucks County, Pennsylvania.

*SPURS, owned by Mr. Lawrence J. Morris.

JACOB HURD—Boston

b. 1702 d. 1758   working dates c. 1725

Hurd was born in Charleston, Massachusetts, February 12, 1702. He held responsible civic positions—First sergeant of Artillery Company, 1745, and Captain in the Militia. He had two sons, Nathaniel and Benjamin, who were also Goldsmiths, but Nathaniel was more famous for his copper plate engravings.

*PORRINGER, lent by Mrs. H. Norris Harrison. It is engraved: "Temperance Clap, 1703; Temperance Clap, 1732; Anna Prescott, 1762; Hannah Prescott, 1792; Mary Ann Bissell, 1815; Edith Parker, 1850; Margaret Stimson, 1872; Marjorie Butler Harrison, 1889."

*PAP BOAT, owned by Mrs. William Rotch Wister. It is marked I.M.C. to M.C. for John and Mary Channing to Mary Channing. They married in 1746. Mary was the daughter of Ninyon Chaloner of Newport and had already been married to Dr. James Robinson. After the fashion of the times she named one of her Channing children, James Robinson Channing. Their daughter, Mary, married, November 19th, 1768, George Gibbs of

Newport, Rhode Island.   Their daughter, Ruth Gibbs, married the Reverend William Ellery Channing.

ISAAC HUTTON—Albany, New York

b. 1767 d. 1855   working date 1790

Opened a shop in 1790.   Worked with his brother George in 1799.   Was Treasurer of the Albany Mechanical Society.

TEASPOONS, two, lent by Mrs. Roy Arthur Hunt, who says that her silver belonged to the Hunt, McQuesten and Thatcher families and to the Hanchett family of East Douglass, Mass.

JOHN JENKINS—Philadelphia

working dates 1777–1796

*MUSTARD SPOON, lent by Mr. and Mrs. Christian Febiger. The original owners were Christian Febiger (1746–96) and his wife, Elizabeth Carson Febiger (1754–1817). See history under Joseph Lownes.

CORNELIUS KIERSTEADE—New York & New Haven

b. 1675 d. 1757   working date 1698

First worked in New York; came to New Haven about 1722.   His shop and house were located in 1724 on the west side of Church street.

*TANKARD, lent by Mrs. Campbell Madeira, deceased.

SAMUEL KIRK—Baltimore

b. 1792 d. 1872   working dates 1815–1872

Samuel Kirk was a native of Doylestown, Pennsylvania. Mr. J. Hall Pleasants in his "Maryland Silversmiths" tells us that he learned his trade in Philadelphia from James Howell. He was of Quaker parentage, descended from English Goldsmiths. He came to Baltimore in 1815. He established the oldest firm of Silversmiths in America, a grandson and great grandson being in the business.

CAN, lent by Mrs. N. E. Bartlett.

E. K. LAKEMAN—Salem, Massachusetts

working date c. 1830

SUGAR SIFTER, lent by Miss Clarissa T. Chase.

JOHN LEACOCK—Philadelphia

working dates 1751–1799

The Pennsylvania Gazette for June 27, 1751, announces that "John Leacock, Goldsmith, is removed from Second street to the Sign of the Cup in Water street, Philadelphia, where he continues to carry on the business as before, and gentlemen may be supplied with all sorts of new and fashionable plate, at the most reasonable rates, and may depend upon its being done in the neatest manner. N.B. He likewise has some goldsmiths tools to dispose of viz:—Raising and bellying anvils, bottom stakes, binding wire, crucibles, files, etc."

Again, in the Pennsylvania Gazette for May 15, 1757, he advertises: "At the Sign of the Cup, in Front-street,

Philadelphia; Variety of Silver-mounted Small Swords, either chased, gadroon, or fluted, or plain. Likewise all Sorts of Gold and Silver Work, at the most reasonable Rates."

GRAVY BOAT, lent by Mrs. James de W. Cookman, deceased.

*SUGAR BOWL WITH LID, lent by Mr. Robert R. Logan.

CHARLES LE ROUX—New York

b. 1689 d. 1745   working dates c. 1715–1745

Practiced his trade before being admitted a freeman, February 16, 1724. Elected Deacon of the New York School same year. Assistant Alderman of the East Ward 1735–8. Commissioned by Common Council to prepare a gold box to enclose the Seal of the City to be presented to George Clinton, September 29, 1743.

*SAUCE BOATS, pair, lent by Mr. Robert R. Logan. These are very unusual pieces, showing French influence.

JOHN LETELIER—Philadelphia

working dates 1770–1793

Advertising, January 29, 1770, in the Pennsylvania Chronicle, he makes, among a long list of articles, the following: "Sauce and cream boats, salts, plain and pierced, castors and nurl'd salts, silver shoe, knee and stock buckles. Surgeons instruments made in silver, mourning rings neatly made—plain gold breast buckles—silver thimbles."

The Philadelphia Directory for 1793 lists him as working at No. 172 North Front street.

*WASTE BOWL, lent by Mrs. Alfred C. Prime. This piece has a splayed foot, applied band at edge and base and large monogram, "C.S." This may stand for Clifford Smith, one of her maternal ancestors.

This item was almost omitted! "Ran away, on Monday, the 14th instant (July) from John Le Telier, Silversmith opposite the Coffee-house, in Market-street, Philadelphia, a Negroe wench, named Nell . . . etc."—Pennsylvania Gazette, August 6, 1777.

HARVEY LEWIS—Philadelphia

working dates 1811–1825

Listed in Philadelphia Directory for 1816 as working at 12 South Second street.

SIX PIECE SERVICE, lent by Miss Edith Markoe Bache who says: "The Harvey Lewis silver service was part of the wedding silver of Mary Ann Cooper, daughter of Daniel Cooper and Elizabeth Rodgers Cooper, who in her twentieth year married William Carman in 1814. The service has descended to the eldest daughter of the eldest daughter for the three succeeding generations."

SEVEN PIECE TEA AND COFFEE SET, lent by Mrs. Frederick Fraley. The original owners were John U. and Elizabeth Fraley.

COFFEE POT, lent by Mrs. Russell Duane. This was presented to Mr. Duane's ancestor, Mr. Inskip, President of the Insurance Company of North America, in recognition of his services.

TEA URN, lent by Mr. Edward Carey Gardiner. The manufacturers of Wilmington gave this to Mathew Carey.

CREAMER, lent by Mrs. Mantle Fielding.

COFFEE POT, lent by Mrs. T. Wistar Brown.

SERVICE OF *COFFEE POT, *TEA POT, *CREAMER, *SUGAR BOWL AND *SAUCE BOAT, lent by Miss Lydia Fisher Warner. Engraved with the kingfish, crest of the Fisher family. It was made from Mexican dollars. The set belonged to her grandmother, Lydia Fisher, born February 9th, 1788, and died January 5, 1850, for whom Miss Warner was named. Lydia Fisher married Benjamin Warner (born May 18th, 1786, and died September 24, 1821) on September 22, 1814. Benjamin Warner was the son of John and Sarah (Christie) Warner.

LEWIS AND SMITH—Philadelphia

working dates 1805–11

Located at 2 South Second street till 1811.

BOWL WITH HANDLE, lent by Mrs. Evan Randolph. Height 5¾ inches, including handle, diameter 4¾ inches, in trefoil design, gadroon edge, and small curved base. The initials are A.R. The bowl was originally given to Anna Roche at the time of her marriage to Andrew Robeson by his sister, Sarah Ann Robeson Lea. In 1924 it was purchased from the widow of Robeson Sargent (great grandson of Andrew Robeson) by Anna Lea Carson, who was the granddaughter of Sarah Ann Robeson Lea and who later gave it to her daughter, Hope Carson Randolph.

SUGAR BOWL WITH LID, lent by Mrs. Walter Penn Shipley.

*HELMET CREAMER, lent by Mrs. Harrold E. Gillingham. Engraved R.H. for Rebecca Harrold.

*URN SHAPED SUGAR BOWL, lent by Mrs. Harrold E. Gillingham. Engraved R.H. for Rebecca Harrold.

CREAMER, lent by Mrs. Walter S. McInnes.
SALT SPOONS, two, lent by Mrs. Wilson McCredy.
PITCHER, lent by Mrs. Walter T. Moore.
CREAMER, lent by Mrs. William Wistar Comfort.

JOSEPH LORING—Boston

b. 1743 d. 1815   working dates 1788–1796

Joseph Loring was born in Hull, Massachusetts.   Served in the Revolutionary War as Lieutenant.

SPOON, lent by Mrs. Henry P. Glendinning.   It was given to Ephraim Langdon Frothingham in 1820.   Mary Foster Frothingham received it as a gift in 1886.   She gave it to the present owner.

EDWARD LOWNES—Philadelphia

working dates 1817–1833

Listed as working at 10½ South Third street in 1820.

SUGAR BOWL, lent by Miss Elizabeth Lea, deceased.
COFFEE POT, lent by Mrs. David Paul Brown.
THREE MUGS, straight sides, lent by Mrs. William Norton Johnson.
CREAMER, owned by Mrs. William Hartzell.
TABLESPOONS, DESSERT SPOONS, TEA SPOONS, SALT SPOONS and SUGAR TONGS, lent by Mrs. William Wistar Comfort.   Engraved E.B.M. for Elizabeth Buckley Morris.
SALT SPOON, lent by Mrs. William Wistar Comfort.   Engraved S.F. for Susan Foulke.
FISH KNIFE, lent by Mr. and Mrs. Rodney C. Cookman.

COFFEE POT and SUGAR BOWL, lent by Mr. and Mrs. Arnold Gindrat Talbot. They belonged to Charlotte Richmond who married Charles Nicholl Talbot in 1833. Their son, William Richmond, married Mary Cornelia Arnold in 1861. Their son, Arnold Gindrat Talbot, married Katherine Streeper Monaghan in 1901. This sugar bowl was constantly borrowed by the Old Presbyterian Church on Bleeker street near South Fifth Avenue, New York, for baptisms.

JOSEPH LOWNES—Philadelphia

working dates 1780–1816

Lownes advertises as working at 130 south Front street from 1791–99. In an advertisement in the Federal Gazette for April 2, 1792: "Joseph Lownes, Goldsmith, No. 130 South Front street, near the Drawbridge, still continues to carry on his business in all its branches; and has now made and ready for sale, Silver Coffee Pots, Tea do., Sugar Basons, Slop bowls, Tankards, Canns, Caddys, Milk pots, Soupe ladles, Table spoons, Tea do., Shoe and knee buckles, also a variety of jewellery & & &."

CAUDLE CUP, lent by Mrs. James de W. Cookman, deceased. It is engraved M.L.

*CAN, lent by Mrs. Frank B. Gummey. She thinks it belonged to her great, great grandfather, Anthony Cadwallader Morris.

SUGAR TONGS, lent by Miss Edith Markoe Bache.

COFFEE URN, SUGAR BOWL and WASTE BOWL, lent by Miss Clarissa T. Chase. The pieces are engraved A.S.M. and belonged to Hester Stork, great, great maternal grandmother of Miss Chase.

CAKE BASKET, lent by Miss Anna H. Howell, deceased.

TABLESPOON, DESSERT SPOONS and TEA SPOONS, lent by Mrs. Charles M. Lea.

TEA POT, SUGAR BOWL and CREAMER, lent anonymously.

TEA CADDY SPOON, lent by Mr. Joseph Carson.

TEA SPOON, lent by Mrs. William Wistar Comfort. Engraved "E.B.M." for Elizabeth Buckley Morris.

SILVER SERVICE, *COFFEE POT, *TEAPOT, *WASTE BOWL, *CREAMER, SUGAR TONGS, TABLESPOONS, DESSERT SPOONS and *LARGE WATER PITCHER, lent by Mr. and Mrs. Christian Febiger. The original owners were Christian Febiger (1746–1796) and his wife, Elizabeth Carson Febiger.

HISTORY OF CHRISTIAN FEBIGER

Born on Island of Funen, Denmark, in 1746.

Came to America as Aide to his uncle, the Governor of Santa Cruz, West Indies.

Engaged in trading between Danish West Indies and Boston.

Commissioned Lieutenant by Committee of Safety in Boston, April 28, 1775 and fought at Bunker Hill.

Commissioned Major, September, 1775.

With Arnold's expedition to Quebec as Adjutant and taken prisoner at the assault on December 31, 1775. Paroled, August 10, 1776 and released from parole January 1, 1777.

Commissioned Lieutenant-Colonel and assigned to General Morgan's Virginia 11th Continentals, January 1, 1777.

Fought at Brandywine; encamped at Valley Forge; fought at Germantown and Monmouth.

Commissioned Colonel in command of 2nd Virginia Regiment of the line, October 2, 1778.

In command of right wing at capture of Stony Point, July 16, 1779. After the battle he and General Wayne exchanged swords. The day following the midnight capture of Stony Point he wrote to his wife:

"My dear Girl,—I have just borrowed pen, ink and paper to inform you that yesterday we marched from Fort Montgomery, and at 12 o'clock last night we stormed this confounded place, and with about fourteen killed and forty or fifty wounded we carried it. I can give you no particulars as yet. A mosquoet ball scraped my nose, no other damage to old Denmark. God bless you. Farewell.

Febiger"

In charge of recruiting of troops and military supplies in Virginia 1780–81 and was present at Cornwallis' surrender at Yorktown, October 19, 1781.

Commissioned Brigadier-General by brevet September 30, 1783.

Captain First Troop Philadelphia City Cavalry, 1790–94.

Treasurer of Pennsylvania, 1789–96.

Married Elizabeth Carson, August 14, 1777.

Died at Philadelphia, September 20, 1796 and buried in Mount Vernon Cemetery.

Sugar Bowl, Creamer and Teapot, anonymous loan.
*Tankard, lent by Mr. Samuel J. Henderson, who tells us: "This tankard was the property of the Reverend Dr. Samuel Jones, who was Minister of the Lower Dublin Baptist Church near Bustleton, Philadelphia. This Church is now (June 4–5, 1938) celebrating its 250th anniversary. The tankard was presented to Dr. Jones by his congregation. He preached at this church for

51 years from 1763 to 1814 (the date of his death), except during the Revolution when he was a chaplain in General Washington's division at Valley Forge.

"Dr. Jones was educated at the College of Philadelphia, now the University of Pennsylvania, and graduated with a degree of Bachelor of Arts in 1761 and three years later received from the same college the degree of Master of Arts. Subsequently, the honorary degree of Doctor of Divinity was conferred on Dr. Jones by both the College of Philadelphia and the University of Rhode Island, now Brown University, which latter university about this time urged him to accept the presidency, but he declined.

"Dr. Jones was descended from a long line of Welsh Baptist Ministers. His father, the Reverend Thomas Jones, came to this country from Wales and founded the Tulpehocken Baptist church at Sinking Springs, Pennsylvania, in 1738 and preached there until his death."

CREAMER and WASTE BOWL, lent by The Misses Huston.

TABLESPOONS, two, lent by Mr. and Mrs. C. Jared Ingersoll.

*COFFEE POT, lent by Mrs. Henry Burnett Robb.

COFFEE POT, TEA POT, CREAMER, SUGAR BOWL, WASTE BOWL and TEA CADDY, lent by Mrs. Logan MacCoy. This set was given by the Misses Hughes to Mary Hollingsworth as a wedding present in 1799.

TEASPOONS, two, lent by Miss Sarah Agnes Morison. Belonged to her great, great grandmother, Agnes Lowndes.

LONG HANDLED SERVING SPOON, lent by Mrs. Alfred C. Prime.

TABLESPOONS, two, lent by Mrs. Alfred C. Prime.

DESSERT SPOONS, two, and TABLESPOONS, two, lent by Mrs. Evan Randolph. The initials are S.H. The spoons are part of the wedding silver of Sarah Humphreys who married Henry Hollingsworth, October 6, 1805. They were inherited by their twin daughters, Hannah and Mary, whose daughters, Anna Stewardson and Susan Carson, respectively, gave them to their cousin and niece, Hope Carson Randolph.

TANKARD and *LADLE, lent by Mrs. Henry B. Robb. They belonged to her great, great grandfather, Nathaniel Mitchell. In 1780–1781 he was Brigade Major. In 1782, Prisoner of War on Parole. He was delegate to the First Continental Congress in Delaware, 1786–88 and Governor of Delaware, 1805–1808, and also a member of the Delaware Society of the Cincinnati.

CREAMER, lent by Mrs. James W. Wister. It was part of the wedding silver of her great grandmother, Elizabeth Bayard and Charles J. Yard, 1789. Elizabeth Bayard was the daughter of Adam and Rebecca Bayard of Wilmington, Delaware. Charles J. Yard was the son of Isaiah Yard and Helena Jones Yard, and the great grandson of William Yarde who with Sir William Trent settled Trenton, New Jersey. They drew lots for the naming of the town and Trent won, so William Yarde settled Yardley across the river. The Yardes were descended from the Norman Baron of that name who crossed to England with William the Conqueror.

WASTE BOWL, lent by Mrs. Horatio Curtis Wood. Ann Pancoast was the original owner.

*SUGAR URN and *WASTE BOWL, lent by Mrs. M. Stevenson Easby. Susanna Waln Hartshorne was the daughter of Robert and Rebecca Waln and granddaughter of Nicholas Waln who came over to America with William Penn on the "Welcome." She married Patterson Hartshorne, son of Hugh and Hannah Hartshorne of the

Borough of Bristol, County of Bucks, Pennsylvania, December 10th, 1776. Patterson and Susanna Hartshorne were the original owners.

*Bowl, owned by Mr. May Stevenson Easby. The bowl has a beaded edge and is engraved with a lion which is the Phillips crest. The original owner was John Phillips, born 1739 and died 1806.

A Portrait of Joseph Lownes is listed with silver in the back of the book. It is photographed from a copy in the possession of Mr. R. Wistar Harvey whose grandmother was a Miss Lownes, a daughter of Joseph Lownes.

(?) LOWNES—Philadelphia

Sugar Urn, lent by Mrs. Henry Paul Busch.

PETER LUPP—New Brunswick, New Jersey

working date 1797–1827

Tablespoon, lent by Mrs. Charles Conrad. It belonged to her great grandmother, Jane Bergen, who married William Wilson. Their home was near New Brunswick. The spoon is engraved I.B.

JOHN LYNCH—Baltimore

b. 1761 d. 1848   working dates 1786–1848

"John Lynch was listed as a silversmith, and a clock and watch-maker. . . . He made a great deal of silver, especially in the first thirty or forty years of his career."— From "Maryland Silversmiths" by Mr. J. Hall Pleasants.

TABLESPOONS, two, lent by Mrs. Carroll Williams, owned by her ancestors who came from Maryland and Virginia.

*COFFEE POT, owned by Mrs. Joseph Harrison. This piece came from the family of James and Elizabeth (Poultney) Large who were married January 15, 1817.

CHARLES MAYSENHOELDER—Philadelphia

working dates 1810–1825

PAIR OF SPECTACLES, lent by Mrs. Walter S. McInnes.

JOHN McMULLIN—Philadelphia

working dates 1795–1841

He worked at 120 South Front street from 1795 to 1800.

SOUP SPOONS, lent by Mrs. Henry D. Paxson, deceased.

SUGAR BOWL, lent by Mr. and Mrs. Rodney P. Cookman.

TEA SERVICE, lent by Mrs. Edwin M. Chance. It was a wedding present to Mary R. Budd who married Dr. Thomas D. Mitchell at the Lazarette, October 18, 1814. At her death the silver was put in safe deposit where it remained for 60 years and is only being used again recently, when Mr. Chance inherited it.

COFFEE POT, TEA POT, WASTE BOWL, SUGAR BOWL and HOT WATER POT, lent by Mrs. T. Wistar Brown.

*SUGAR URN, *HELMET CREAMER and *BILL for same, lent by Mrs. Alfred C. Prime. These pieces were given to her by her husband. The bill reads as follows:

"Philadelphia December 11th, 1802

Miss Mary Hutton

  Bot. of John McMullin

One silver sugar dish........Dolls.	28.25
One Cream pot...................	13.25
Six tea spoons....................	6.00
One pair of Sugar tongs...........	4.25
Engraving do do.................	2.50
	$ 54.25

Received the above in full for

  John McMullin—Thomas Perkins"

Unfortunately the teaspoons and the sugar tongs have gone elsewhere and are no longer with the other pieces.

SPOON, lent by The Misses Huston.

SOUP LADLE, with bright cutting and LARGE SPOON, lent by Mrs. Harrold E. Gillingham.

EDMUND MILNE—Philadelphia

b. 1724 d. 1822   working dates 1757–1773

He advertises at the Crown and three Pearls, next door to the corner of Market street, in Second-street. . . . He seems to have imported a great deal of silver, and in one of his advertisements speaks of "Intending for England." He advertised in the Staatsbote, the German newspaper of the day, and also we find his notices in the Maryland Gazette for January and May, 1764. Although the following advertisement does not throw much light on Mr. Milne it is interesting and worthy of record: "Five Pounds Reward. Stolen about the 5th of May last, out of the shop of Gabriel Lewyn, Goldsmith and Jeweller, in Baltimore-Town, by a person unknown, an Ingot of Gold, weighing about 5 ounces, thick in the middle and narrow towards each end, and between 5 and 6 inches long. Reward to be paid by Mr. Edmond Milne, Goldsmith, in Philadelphia, or Mr. Gabriel Lewyn, in Baltimore-Town, Maryland."— Pennsylvania Gazette, June 13, 1771.

It is interesting to know that Edmund Milne made several camp cups for George Washington. A good many silver articles were used in trading with the Indians and were made especially for them. A number of these pieces were made by this craftsman.

*SMALL DRINKING CUP, lent by Mrs. Harrold E. Gillingham.

*BRANDY WARMER, lent by Mrs. Thornton Oakley, who writes: "This Brandy warmer belonged to my great, great grandfather, James Hunter, Merchant, who built Woodstock (the house where I live at Villa Nova) in 1776. We have a letter signed by Tench Tilghman from Headquarters at Valley Forge, February 7, 1778, to the officer commanding the Radnor Picket from which the following is quoted: 'The bearer Mr. James Hunter of Philadelphia . . . as this gentleman has been obliged to fly from Philadelphia he has been under the necessity of purchasing provisions for the subsistance of his family and as he has already spared the army a full proportion of what he had laid up for his family it is his Excellency's order that no more provision be taken from him on any account. . . .'

"James Hunter was born in Scotland in 1729 and died in Philadelphia on February 26, 1796. His wife was Elinor Gardiner. His daughter, Jane, married Maskell Ewing of Trenton, New Jersey, whose son, Maskell Cochran Ewing was the father of my father, James Hunter Ewing."

*PORRINGER, owned by the family of the late William Rotch Wister. It is the keyhole type and engraved D.L.W. for Daniel and Lowry (Jones) Wister, daughter of Owen Jones of Lower Merion Township, Montgomery County, first Colonial Treasurer. She was born in 1742 and married Daniel Wister, son of John Wister, in 1760. She died in 1805.

MOORE AND FERGUSON—Philadelphia

working dates 1801–1805

*HELMET CREAMER, lent by Mrs. Horatio Curtis Wood. It was the property of Hannah Cooper, as shown by large initials engraved on one side. She was the daughter of Marmaduke and Mary Jones Cooper, and lived with her parents in the Cooper Mansion, Camden, New Jersey, dying unmarried. The Cooper Mansion now belongs to the City of Camden and stands in a park. At one time it was occupied by the Camden Historical Society.

The next owner of the creamer was a sister, Margaret Cooper, who married Israel Cope. Through their daughter, Elizabeth Cope Collins, it came to her grandson, the present owner, Edward Cope Wood.

MUSTARD SPOON, lent by Mrs. Wilson McCredy.

CREAMER, lent by Mrs. Walter S. McInnes.

JOSEPH MOULTON—Newburyport, Massachusetts

b. 1694 c. 1756

Miss C. Louise Avery in "American Silver of the XVII and XVIII Centuries" says: "Joseph Moulton was born in

Newbury, Massachusetts and moved to Newburyport. He began the business of silversmithing which was carried on by six successive generations. Joseph was a blacksmith as well as a goldsmith."

TEASPOON, lent by the Misses Hannah C. and Margaret E. Wright. It is attributed to Joseph Moulton.

JOHN MURDOCH—Philadelphia

working dates 1779–1785

Listed in Philadelphia Directory as working at Front between Walnut and Spruce streets in 1785.

PORRINGER, lent by Mrs. Horatio Curtis Wood. The original owner was Israel Morris. Engraved "I.M."

JAMES MUSGRAVE—Philadelphia

working dates 1795–1811

He advertises in the Gazette of the United States (Philadelphia) as follows: "James Musgrave, Goldsmith and Jeweller, No. 42 south Second-street. . . . All kinds of work in gold and silver line; miniatures set, and hair work executed as usual."—November 19, 1796.

CUP, lent by Mrs. Francis Olcott Allen.

COFFEE POT, TEA POT, CREAMER, SUGAR BOWL WITH LID and WASTE BOWL, lent by Mr. Barry Hepburn who writes: "Made for Patrick Hayes, my great grandfather, a sea captain engaged in the trade with China. He sailed as a cabin boy with his Uncle, Commodore John Barry. He had the honor of carrying the first million dollar cargo to China."

JOHN MYERS—Philadelphia

working dates 1785–1804

Advertises as follows: "John Myers, Goldsmith, Returns thanks to his Friends and the Public in general, for past favors, and begs leave to inform them, that he has removed from his late dwelling house in Second street, to the north side of Market street, between Second and Third streets, where he continues his Business in all its various branches, and upon the most reasonable terms. Any favours conferred upon him will be attended to with punctuality and dispatch.

"And also a neat assortment of Dry Goods, suitable to the season.

"N.B. Stopped from a suspicious person, a Silver Tablespoon, supposed to have been stolen. Any person proving property may have it again, by applying as above."
—Pennsylvania Packet, June 23, 1787.

John Myers was an apprentice of Richard Humphreys.

SUGAR TONGS, lent by Misses Hannah C. and Margaret E. Wright.

MYER MYERS—New York

working dates 1745–1802

Admitted freeman, April 29, 1745. . . . President of the New York Silver Smiths Society in 1776. In 1786 he worked at Greenwich Street. . . . Was a prominent Master Mason. Of the firm Hays and Myers.

PIE KNIFE, lent by Mr. and Mrs. David B. Robb. It belonged to Jasper Yeates, born 1745 and died 1817. He married Sarah Burd, great granddaughter of Edward

Shippen of Philadelphia who was Speaker of Assembly
in 1695 and first Mayor of Philadelphia and President of
Council.   Mary Yeates married Charles Smith.   Wil-
liaminia E. Smith married Thomas B. McElwee.   Sarah
Yeates McElwee married Townsend Whelen.   Sarah
Yeates Whelen married Edward Tunis Bruen.   Edith
Guest Bruen married Joseph Carson.   Sarah Whelen
Carson married David B. Robb.

WILLIAM S. NICHOLS—Newport, Rhode Island

b. 1785 d. 1871   working date 1808

Born in Providence.   Apprentice to Thomas Arnold.
Began business in 1808.   Located at 155 Thames street in
1842.

SALT SPOONS, two, lent by Mrs. William Wistar Comfort.
Engraved "M.E." for Mary Engs.

BASSETT NICHOLS—Providence, Rhode Island

                                working date 1815

LADLE, lent by Mrs. William Wistar Comfort.

JOHANNIS NYS—Philadelphia

                           working dates 1700–c. 1723

There is little known about this early silversmith.   Mr.
Harrold E. Gillingham in his research work has discovered
the following facts.   Among the miscellaneous manu-
scripts at the Historical Society there is a list of the early

craftsmen in Philadelphia: "Silversmiths, Cezor Ghisling, John Denise, 1698."

Penn's cash book mentions "Johan Nys ye Goldsmith, 2 Mo. 22, 1700." There is in an Account Book and Ledger at the Historical Society under date of 9 Mo. 5th, 1700, this item: "To three silver porringers pd. his order given my wife & two spoons £9.12.9, To Proffitt and Loss pd. John Nys for making three porringers £1.9.9"

In 1710, Johannis Nys, Francis Richardson and Cesar Ghiselin, with many other prominent citizens, signed a petition of the Inhabitants of Philadelphia to the General Assembly for more liberal Corporation powers for the city. He must have been working in 1722, for in James Logan's Ledger B, page 125, 6 Mo. 6, 1722, there is an account of Plate, "paid Jno. Nyse in full £1.8.0." On July 8, 1723, he witnessed the will of John Goadby (Book D, p. 361). So far, this is the last date found concerning Johannis Nys.

In September, 1933, there was a loan Exhibit of silver made by Nys, held at the Gallery of Fine Arts at Yale University. In their Bulletin published that month, Mr. John Marshall Phillips describes many of the pieces. There were eighteen assembled at that time—"Five tankards, seven porringers, a waiter and five spoons."

PORRINGER, lent by Mrs. James de W. Cookman, deceased. Engraved E.G.

*PORRINGERS, two, lent by Dr. George Morrison Coates. They belonged to his seventh great grandfather. The handles are of the early geometric type and they are engraved T.C.B. for Thomas and Beulah Coates.

*SPOON, lent by Mr. Robert R. Logan. It is of rat tail type and engraved M.L.

TANKARD, lent anonymously.

*TANKARD, lent by The Historical Society of Pennsylvania. Mr. John Marshall Phillips describes this piece as follows: "Of equal interest is the Emelen tankard, belonging to the transitional period, having the domed top and scrolled thumbpiece characteristic of English silver under Queen Anne, but retaining the beaded rat tail on the handle and the cast head on the handletip in the New York tradition. This was made for George and Mary Emelen, who were married in 1717, and bears their cypher."

*PORRINGER, lent by Mrs. Arthur Howell.

*SUCKET FORK, gift to the Philadelphia Museum of Art by Mrs. Alfred Coxe Prime. It has a spoon at one end and two tined fork at the other. It was used for sweet meats and is very rare.

PETER OLIVER—Boston, Massachusetts

b. 1682 d. 1712

CHOCOLATE POT, anonymous loan. This is a rare and unusual piece.

JONATHAN OTIS—Newport, Rhode Island

b. 1723 d. 1791

Born in Sandwich, Massachusetts. Began business in Newport, Rhode Island, where he continued to work until 1778. Commander of the militia with the rank of Major. During British invasion removed to Middletown where he died in 1791.

LARGE BASTING SPOON, anonymous loan. It has a round hollow handle with ring attached.

JESSE OWEN—Philadelphia

d. 1794

He worked in Priests Alley.

TABLESPOON, engraved M.T., lent by Mrs. Henry Paxson, deceased.

*LADLE, lent by Miss Xenia C. Clampitt. Belonged to Richard Leedom, of Wrightstown, Pennsylvania. His daughter, Rachel, married John Thomas of Bucks County. Their son, John, was the grandfather of the present owner.

SUGAR BOWL, lent by Mrs. Ninian C. Cregar.

SAMUEL PANCOAST—Philadelphia

working dates 1785, 1795

Listed in the Philadelphia Directories as working at 134 South Front street in 1793.

*SUGAR BOWL, lent by Mrs. William Wistar Comfort. Engraved "A.P." for Ann Pancoast.

*CREAMER, lent by Mrs. Raymond Shortlidge.

PARRY AND MUSGRAVE—Philadelphia

working dates 1793, 1796

This firm advertises in the Gazette of the United States for December 24, 1793, as follows: "Parry and Musgrave, Goldsmiths & Jewellers, No.42, South Second street, Have for sale, An elegant Assortment of Silver and Plated Ware, Jewellery and fine Cutlery.

"Which they will dispose of on the most reasonable

terms.   Devices in hair, Miniatures sett, and everything in the gold and silver way, done as usual."

The partnership did not last long, however, for we find they announced on November 10, 1795, that "The partnership of Parry and Musgrave is this day dissolved; all persons indebted to, or who have any demands on said firm, will please apply for settlement, to

Rowland Parry,

No. 36, Chesnut St.

or to James Musgrave."

COFFEE SPOONS, lent by Mrs. Henry B. Robb.

JOHN PEARSON—New York

working date 1791

TEASPOONS, lent by Mrs. William Doughten.

HENRY I. PEPPER—Philadelphia

working dates 1828, 1850

BUTTER KNIFE, lent by Mrs. Walter S. McInnes.

WILLIAM PITKIN—East Hartford, Connecticut

Unfortunately there were two William Pitkins, one William J. and the other William L.   It is not certain which made the spoon.   There are several marks which read "W.Pitkin."   Therefore, there is doubt about this piece.

SPOON, lent by Mrs. Roy Arthur Hunt who says her silver belonged to the Hunt, McQuesten, and Thatcher families and to the Hanchett family of East Douglass, Massachusetts.

ANTHONY RASCH—Philadelphia
working dates 1807–09, 13–19

Worked at No. 4 Watkins Alley in 1809.   Of the Firms
Rasch & Willing and Chaudron & Rasch.

TEAPOT, lent by Mrs. Joseph Linden Heacock.
BABY MUG, lent by Miss Ida Elizabeth Rhoad.   Belonged
   to John Ashurst, great, great grandfather of Miss Rhoad.

PAUL REVERE—Boston, Massachusetts
b. 1735 d. 1818

Son of the Hugenot Silversmith, Apollos Rivoire, as he
was known, till he changed his name to simpler Paul
Revere.   He learned his trade in his fathers shop.   He
took a very active part in national and civic affairs, beginning by participating in the expedition for the capture of
Crown Point, 1756.   He was a copper plate engraver as
well as a silversmith and engraved the plates for the earliest
paper currency of Massachusetts.   He resumed business
after the Revolution, in 1783, at 50 Cornhill street.   His
son, Paul Revere, was also a silversmith.

CREAMER, lent by Mrs. E. Walter Clark, deceased.
*TEA POT, *SUGAR BOWL, and *URN WITH *LEDGER, lent
   by Mrs. Charles F. Russell, deceased.   These pieces are
   now owned by Miss Frances R. Porter and Mrs. William
   Stanley Parker.   The original owner was Benjamin Lin-
   coln.   This silver come down in direct line to them.

JOSEPH RICE—Baltimore
working dates 1784–1801

Joseph Rice, Mr. J. Hall Pleasants tells us, advertised as

a watch and clock maker. For two years he was in part-nership with Standish Barry, another silversmith. They engraved copper plates as well as making and repairing gold and silver work.

DESSERT SPOON, lent by Mr. and Mrs. Arnold Gindrat Talbot. It was owned by Louisa Caroline Gindrat who married Richard James Arnold, 1823. Their daughter, Mary Cornelia Arnold, married William Richmond Tal-bot in 1861. Their son, Arnold Gindrat Talbot, mar-ried Katherine Streeper Monaghan in 1901.

SAMUEL RICHARDS—Philadelphia

working dates 1791–1818

Advertised as working at 136 South Front street in 1793.

TABLESPOON, lent by Mr. and Mrs. Arnold Gindrat Talbot. It belonged to Governor Simeon Martin, brother of Sylvanus Martin, who married Amey Brown. Their daughter, Amey, married Samuel N. Richmond in 1806. Their daughter, Charlotte, married Charles Nicholl Tal-bot in 1833. Their son, William Richmond, married Mary Cornelia Arnold in 1861. Their son, Arnold Gin-drat Talbot, married Katherine Streeper Monaghan in 1901.

COFFEE POT, lent by Mrs. William Norton Johnson.

TEA POT and PITCHER, lent by Mrs. William Norton Johnson.

TEAPOT, Engraved R.L., lent anonymously.

SUGAR URN, lent by Mr. and Mrs. Stanley Eyre Wilson. It belonged to Susanna Pusey, great grandmother of Mr. Wilson.

SUGAR BOWL, lent by Miss Hannah C. Wright and Miss Margaret E. Wright.

SMALL SPOONS, lent anonymously.

RICHARDS AND WILLIAMSON—Philadelphia

working dates 1797–1800

As they give their address as 136 South Front street in 1797 Samuel Richards must have gone into partnership.

TANKARD, lent by Mrs. Henry B. Robb.

CREAMER, lent by The Misses Hannah C. and Margaret E. Wright.

CREAMER, lent by Miss Sarah Agnes Morison. Belonged to Mary Cocke Morison, great grandmother of Miss Morison.

CREAMER, lent by Mr. and Mrs. Arnold Gindrat Talbot.

THE RICHARDSON FAMILY

From notes taken from the book edited by Mary T. Seaman, published in 1929, and material furnished by Mr. Harrold E. Gillingham.

There were five silversmiths in the family, working in three generations. They made a great deal of important silver and their history is worthy of being given in detail.

The Richardson family came to America in June, 1681. The earliest Francis, not a silversmith, of Radcliffe, county of Middlesex, England, married Rebecca Hayward in January, 1680. They were Quakers. Upon their arrival in America they first settled in New York. Francis, the first goldsmith, was born there the year of their arrival in 1681. His father died in 1688. Mrs. Richardson, however, did not remain a widow long. She married, in Rhode Island, in 1689, Edward Shippen. They came to Philadelphia in 1690, and Edward Shippen became very active in civic matters, becoming the first mayor in 1701.

FRANCIS RICHARDSON

b. 1681 d. 1729.   working c. 1700

He came to Philadelphia with his mother and stepfather in 1690. In his youth he went to Europe with a half brother, son of Edward Shippen by a previous marriage, and returning he became a goldsmith of note. On 6th mo. 30, 1705, when 24 years old he married Elizabeth Growden (born in England and died before 1730). She lived in Trevose, Bucks County, Pennsylvania. They had two sons, Francis, Junior, and Joseph (who succeeded his father in business). Elizabeth died and Francis married a second time, Letitia Swift, 4th mo. 30, 1726, who had a son John. Francis died, 6 mo. 17, 1729, and by his will left his oldest son, Francis, 400 acres of land in Kent County on Delaware. To Joseph he bequeathed: "all my working Tools, provided he continue and live with his mother in Law (meaning his step-mother) and carry on my Trade for her until he shall attain the full age of twenty-one years."

Though Francis was not made a freeman till 1717, we find him working in 1700. In William Penn's Cash Book at the American Philosophical Society is the following entry: "1700, September 1, By Letitia, pd ff Richardson for Buckles £2.0.0., 1701, 6 mo. 13, paid ffrs Richardsons note for her (Letitia) £0.5.0." In 1710 he signed the Petition to General Assembly for more liberal Corporation powers.

FRANCIS RICHARDSON II

b. 1708 working in 1736–1745

Francis Richardson, son of the first goldsmith, born in 1708, was the older brother of Joseph Richardson (Senior). He married, 9th mo. 26th, 1742, Mary Fitzwater. They had several children but no sons married. He advertised in the Pennsylvania Gazette for September 9th, 1736: "Francis Richardson, very neat clocks and Jacks made, sold cleaned and mended reasonably by Francis Richardson, Goldsmith at the Corner of Letitia Court in Market Street." Again in April 28, 1737, he inserts the following: "Very neat clocks and Brass Jacks, Handles and Escutchions, Tea Tables Bolts and Desk Hinges to be sold very reasonably by Francis Richardson, Goldsmith in Market street; Also Clocks and Watches cleaned and repaired at the same place."—Pennsylvania Gazette.

On September 12, 1740, there is a record at the Historical Society of Pensylvania of payment: "Received of William Parson £5.1.5, in full of all Accots." Again we find on April 12, 1745: "Received of Benjamin Franklin £7. on account." This is in Franklin's Receipt Book at the American Philosophical Society. So much for the second Francis.

JOSEPH RICHARDSON, Sr.   (Mark I.R.)

b. 1711 d. 1784 working dates 1736–c. 1771

Brother of the Second Francis and father of Joseph, Jr., and Nathaniel. He was named for his maternal grandfather, Joseph Growden. He was born in 1711. He married, 6 mo. 3rd, 1741, Hannah Worrel. They had two daughters. There is no record of this first wife's death. In 1748 on 2 mo. 14th, at the age of 37 he married Mary

Allen, daughter of Nathaniel and Hannah Allen. They
had five children, among them Joseph and Nathaniel.
Joseph Richardson, Sr., died in 1784 and his wife died in
1787. In Joseph's will, proved October 11th, 1784, to his
wife he left his house on Front street, where he lived. To
sons, Joseph and Nathaniel, he left his shop and "my Shew
Glass, working tools and utensils of trade." His shop was
on the west side of Front between Chesnut and Walnut
streets.

It is interesting to note in checking over records that
these early craftsmen carried on an interchange of business together. We find that Joseph Richardson, Senior,
charged Philip Syng, Junior, with many items. One entry
in 1733 is "To a Silver Snuff Box, to fashioning ye bx 12s."
And on the same date Syng is credited with having supplied " A Shell for a Sword hilt" and for "fashing of
Spoons and other things," showing conclusively that they
worked for each other.

In 1756 The Friendly Association for regaining and pre-
serving Peace with the Indians by Pacific Measures was in-
augurated by the most prominent Friends of Philadelphia
and adjacent counties. Their original Minute Book has
recently been secured by the Historical Society of Pennsylvania and Mr. Harrold E. Gillingham has gleaned many
interesting facts from it. Joseph Richardson, Senior, and
Joseph Lownes were both members and contributors to the
Friendly Association. It appears that the former made
large quantities of medals and silver work for presentation
to the Indians. There is a Gorget believed to have been
made for the Friendly Association by Joseph Richardson,
Senior, in the Historical Society of Pennsylvania collection.

Richardson is mentioned among a long list of important
Philadelphians as a signer of the Non-Importation Agreement in 1765.

In James Wharton's Shipchandlery Book, for 1762, page 165, the Ship Delaware is charged: "To cash paid for plate and made a present to Joseph Richardson £10, 16.0."

JOSEPH RICHARDSON, Jr.   (Mark J.R.)

b. 1752 d. 1831   working dates 1777–c. 1805

Son of Joseph Richardson, Sr., and brother of Nathaniel. In 1780 at the age of twenty-eight he married Ruth Hoskins.   The wedding took place at the old meeting house of Friends in Burlington, New Jersey.   Joseph and Nathaniel worked for some years at 50 South Front Street, below Walnut.   It was a low two-story house with extensive buildings in the rear which were their workshop.   From 1798 to 1805 Joseph lived at Green Bank, Burlington, New Jersey.   In 1805 he built a house in Philadelphia between 9th and 10th on Market Street.   This was considered quite far out of town.

When Joseph, Jr., died in 1831 he left in his will "To my son, John, my scales and weights and silver smith Tools and a Silver Cup with General Washington's Arms on." Joseph received his commission of Assayer of the Mint from George Washington, December 12, 1795, and held this position until his death in 1831.

JOSEPH AND NATHANIEL RICHARDSON
(Mark INR)

working dates 1785–1791

Joseph and Nathaniel worked for some years at 50 South Front Street.   Nathaniel is listed later as an ironmonger. He never married and made his home permanently with his brother.   He died August, 1827.

FRANCIS RICHARDSON—Philadelphia

b. 1681 d. 1729   working c. 1700

*PORRINGER, lent by Mrs. William W. Doughten.
SPOON, lent by Mr. Robert R. Logan.
*PORRINGER, lent by Mr. and Mrs. David Buzby Robb.
   The interesting history of the owners of this piece is
   given under their Peter David Tankard.
*TANKARD, lent by Dr. Isaac Starr.

FRANCIS RICHARDSON II—Philadelphia

b. 1708   working in 1736, 1745

*PORRINGER, lent by Mr. and Mrs. C. Jared Ingersoll.

JOSEPH RICHARDSON, Sr.—Philadelphia

b. 1711 d. 1784   working dates 1736–c. 1771
   Mark "I.R."

TANKARD, Chevalier Crest, lent anonymously.
TEA SPOON, lent by Mrs. J. Herman Barnsley, who tells
   us: "It was found last year in a crevice in one of the big
   stone chimneys at the Bird-in-Hand Tavern (built before 1723) in Newtown, Bucks County, Pennsylvania."
CREAMER, lent by Mrs. Gibson Bell. It belonged to her
   great, great, great grandmother, Elizabeth Dawson, and
   has come directly in descent to her.
TEA SPOON, lent by Mrs. William Wistar Comfort. Engraved I.A.E.
PUNCH LADLE, lent by Captain Harry Coleman Drayton.
   Engraved "1762, E.E." for Elizabeth Edwards, a maternal great grandmother. Owned by Palmer Welsh,

Evelyn Welsh Gray, Edith Newbold (Welsh) Drayton, Harry Coleman Drayton.

*Sugar Urn with Cover, lent by Mrs. Charles A. Fife. The original owner was her great, great, great grandfather, James Lea (1723–1798), whose wife was Margaret Marshall Lea. He was chief Burgess of Wilmington in 1768 and 1769 and Treasurer, 1773–1775.

Two Dessert Spoons, lent by Mrs. Harrold E. Gillingham.

Large Spoon, lent by Mrs. Harrold E. Gillingham.

*Hot Water Can, lent by Miss Martha Paul Howell. This can is a small and interesting piece, pear shaped with moulded foot and reeded midband. It has a spout with moulded lip, dome cover and scroll handle. Engraved block letters "E.H." It is 4½ inches high with the maker's mark, I.R., in oval on bottom.

*Milk Can with wooden handle, lent by Miss Martha Paul Howell and owned by Mr. J. Robeson Howell.

Teaspoon, lent by Mrs. A. Sydney Logan, deceased. Engraved H.E. for Hannah Emelen.

Tea Pot, lent by Mrs. A. Sydney Logan, deceased.

*Porringer, lent by Mrs. Joseph B. Hutchinson. It is marked M.E. and was made for Mary Emelen (1746–1820), daughter of George and Ann Emelen who married David Beveridge. It has come down in the fifth generation to Mrs. Hutchinson.

*Salver, lent by Mrs. Francis von A. Cabeen. This is also marked M.E. and is believed to have belonged to the same Mary Emelen who married David Beveridge and owned the porringer inherited by Mrs. Hutchinson.

Porringer, lent by Mr. Charles M. Wistar. Belonged to Caspar and Catherine Wistar, 1735–1740.

Sugar Bowl, lent by Daniel Wister, 2nd, deceased. The bowl is part of the wedding silver of Daniel and Lowry

(Jones) Wister, 1760. Daniel Wister was the son of
John and Anna Catherina (Rubenham) Wister and John
was the son of Hans Caspar and Anna Katerina Wister
of Hillspach, Germany. Lowry Jones was the daughter
of Owen and Susannah Jones and was the great, great
granddaughter of Dr. Thomas Wynne.

TEA SERVICE, SEVEN PIECES, lent by Mr. Roland L. Taylor,
who gives this story about its acquisition.

In 1922 while visiting Crichton's on Old Bond Street,
London, one of the principal salesmen asked him
whether he would like to see their museum, and he, of
course, answered in the affirmative. The first object in
the Museum was a case containing three pieces of the
Richardson silver—the tall coffee pot, sugar bowl and
cream pitcher.

The salesman told him that Mr. Crichton had become
so much interested in making a collection of old American silver for a client that when the work was finished
he started to make a collection for himself and these
three pieces were the beginning.

Mr. Taylor said that if this was his start, he was going
to ask him to make another because he would like to
have these three pieces of silver. As his home was in
Philadelphia it was fitting that the silver should go back
there. The salesman remarked that Mr. Crichton, of
course, would not think of selling what he had bought
for himself, but Mr. Taylor insisted that he should try.
Thereupon Mr. Crichton very courteously allowed him
to have the pieces at a very reasonable price.

Some two years later in passing the show window of
Samuel T. Freeman & Co. he noticed an open catalogue
in which was displayed silver which seemed identical
with the three pieces bought from London. They were

good enough to allow him to take the silver home to show Mrs. Taylor, and he found the marks identical with those upon the pieces he had. Their offering consisted of four pieces—teapot, waste bowl, another creamer and sugar urn. These four pieces had been displayed in the Philadelphia Museum for two years and had letters showing that they had not been out of the possession of the family which they entered as a wedding gift. . . . He was successful in buying these pieces. . . . It seemed rather romantic to pick up half of a complete set in London and half at auction in Philadelphia.

CAN, lent by Mrs. William Norton Johnson.

*COFFEE POT, lent by Miss Hannah C. Wright and Miss Margaret E. Wright. It was left to the first Susanna Wright by Miss Wright's fourth great grandfather. The first Susanna came over to America when she was seventeen. She was the first person to bring silk worms to this country and to make silk. A piece of the latter she sent to Queen Anne who sent her a handsome portfolio. This is now owned by Miss Hannah C. Wright.

*SAUCE BOAT, lent by Mr. Lawrence J. Morris.

TABLESPOON, lent by Mrs. Alfred Coxe Prime. It has a long handle with bright cutting. Engraved "C.B."

TABLESPOON, lent by Mrs. Edward S. Dillon.

CREAMER, PORRINGER, and SOUP LADLE, lent by Miss Lydia Wistar Rhoads.

SAUCE BOAT, lent by Mrs. Henry Pemberton, Jr. This is a fine piece. It is marked with the crest of Israel Pemberton.

CAN, SALVER, PAIR OF SPOONS, and *TEAPOT, lent by Mr. Robert R. Logan. This silver came down through the Logan, Dickinson and Norris families.

JOSEPH RICHARDSON, Jr.—Philadelphia

b 1752 d. 1831   working dates 1777 c 1805

SUGAR TONGS, lent by the Misses Ashbridge.

*SIX DOLL'S TEASPOONS and *DOLL'S SUGAR TONGS, lent by Miss Clarissa T. Chase.   They belonged to Margaret (Hill) Morris, fifth great granddaughter of Governor Thomas Lloyd (1737–1816).   Margaret Morris' husband, William Morris, was a brother of Captain Samuel Morris of the First Troop of Philadelphia City Cavalry.

*FLUTED HELMET CREAMER, lent by Mrs. Harrold E. Gillingham.

COFFEE POT, *TEA POT, *SUGAR BOWL WITH LID, *TEA POT, WASTE BOWL, *SUGAR TONGS, and DOUBLE HANDLED LEMON STRAINER, lent by Mrs. William Norton Johnson.   The original owner was Samuel Wheeler, father of Sarah Wheeler, who married John Johnson in 1800, grandmother of Mr. William Norton Johnson.   The bill is photographed also.

*TANKARD, lent by Miss Augusta C. McMillan, from the estate of Annis Field McMillan.   It originally belonged to Robert Field who married Mary Emmett.   The initials on handle are R.M.F.   It came down to Mrs. McMillan from her father, the Hon. Richard Stockton Field, one time Federal Judge in Washington, who was a descendant of Richard Stockton, one of the signers of the Declaration of Independence.

*SIX SILVER GILT TEASPOONS, lent by Mr. Lawrence J. Morris.

PITCHER, lent by Miss Ella Parsons.

TWO TEASPOONS, lent by Mrs. Henry D. Paxson, deceased.

*CAN AND CREAMER, lent by the Misses Margaret E. Wright and Hannah C. Wright.

PORRINGER, lent anonymously.

*Tea Service, consisting of tea pot, coffee pot, helmet creamer, sugar urn and tea caddy, lent by Mrs. George D. Fowle. The set originally belonged to Thomas Mifflin, First Governor of Pennsylvania (1790–1799).

Dessert Spoons, two, lent by Mrs. R. Wilson McCredy.

*Nutmeg Grater, owned by Mr. Lawrence J. Morris.

Punch Ladle, lent by Mrs. Francis von A. Cabeen, Jr.

Teapot, lent by Mrs. Evan Randolph. Engraved "H.H." It was purchased by Hannah Paschall Hollingsworth and inherited by her son, Henry Hollingsworth; then, by his daughter, Hannah Hollingsworth Stewardson whose daughter, Caroline Stewardson Humphreys, gave it to her first cousin's child, Hope Carson Randolph, whose great grandmother was the original owner.

Pair of Spoons, lent by Mrs. Alfred Coxe Prime. Bright cutting.

Ladle, lent by Mrs. Alfred Coxe Prime.

Can, lent by Mrs. Alfred Coxe Prime. This piece has been repaired by Abraham Carlile who stamped his name over that of Richardson.

Teapot, lent by Mrs. Howard Butcher, Jr.

Creamer and Sugar Tongs, lent by Miss Edith M. Bache. Belonged to Elizabeth Rodgers who married Daniel Cooper on January 9, 1792.

Teaspoon, lent by Miss Sarah Bache Hodge. Engraved "F.H." for Frances Howell, great, great grandmother.

*Cup, owned by Miss Mary Evans. Originally belonged to Mary Benedict, great, great grandmother.

The following pieces are not fully identified, but are attributed to Joseph Richardson, Jr., working 1777, circa 1805.

Coffee Pot, lent by Mrs. Morris Hill Merritt. The following is engraved on the coffee pot: "Mary Smith and

Richard Hill Morris, 1798; Charles M. and Ann J. Morris, 1848; William J. and Anne H. Morris, 1883; James S. and Gertrude R. M. Merritt, 1902; Morris Hill Merritt, 1913, married Sarah Ellen Richardson, November 10, 1928.''

COFFEE POT, lent by Mr. Edward Carey Gardiner.

HELMET CREAMER, lent by Mr. Barry Hepburn.

PITCHER, lent by Mrs. John Harrison, Jr.

TABLESPOONS, lent by Mr. and Mrs. C. Jared Ingersoll.

TEASPOON, lent by Mr. and Mrs. C. Jared Ingersoll.

TEASPOONS, lent by Mrs. Walter S. McInnes.

PAIR OF MUGS, lent by Mrs. B. Brannan Reath, 2nd.

MUG, lent by Mr. and Mrs. David Buzby Robb.   Belonged to Anna Eliza Guest (1798–1859) who married Thomas Roberts Tunis.

"GOLD SCALES AND WEIGHTS SOLD BY JOSEPH RICHARDSON, GOLDSMITH, IN PHILADELPHIA," lent by The Friends Historical Association.   These jeweler's scales and weights belonged to Meirs Fisher (1748–1819). His great granddaughter, Miss Lydia Fisher Warner, has lent them to the Friends Historical Association.

The following "Table of the Value and Weight of Coins as they now pass in Pennsylvania" is taken from the label on the cover of the box containing the scales.

	£	s	d	dwt.	gr.
English Guineas	1	14	0	5	6
French Guineas	1	13	6	5	5
Moydores	2	3	6	6	18
Johannes's	6	0	0	18	0
Half Johannes's	3	0	0	9	0
French Pistoles	1	6	6	4	4
4 Spanish Pistole Pieces	5	8	0	17	0

2 Spanish Pistole Pieces....	2	14	0	8	12
1 Spanish Pistole..........	1	7	0	4	6
Half a Spanish Pistole.....	0	13	6	2	3
C (?) lines............	1	14	0	6	5
Spanish Pieces of Eight....	0	7	6	17	6

JOSEPH AND NATHANIEL RICHARDSON—
Philadelphia

working dates 1785–1791

They advertise in the directory for 1785 as working at Front between Chesnut and Walnut street.

TEAPOT, anonymous loan.

SUGAR BOWL, lent by Mr. and Mrs. Rodney P. Cookman.

TANKARD, lent by Mrs. James de W. Cookman, deceased.

TWO TEASPOONS, lent by Miss Laura Curtis Haines, deceased.

*TEA POT, lent by Mrs. Charles E. Ingersoll.   It has initials J.E.I. for Jared and Elizabeth (Pettit) Ingersoll.   Jared Ingersoll was a signer of the Constitution and was married in 1780 in Philadelphia.

SPOON, lent by Mrs. Drummond W. Little.   It is engraved "J.P."   This was part of Jane Paxson's wedding silver. She was a direct descendant of Evan Oliver and Jean Lloyd who came over on "The Welcome" whose child was born on the voyage and was named "Seaborn."

THREE TABLESPOONS, lent by Mrs. A. Sydney Logan, deceased.   Engraved D.N. for Deborah Norris.

TWO TABLESPOONS, lent by Mrs. Walter S. McInnes.

NUTMEG BOX, lent by Miss Lydia Wistar Rhoads.

PORRINGER, lent by Mrs. John M. Whitall, deceased.

TEAPOT, lent anonymously.

CREAMER, lent by the Misses Hannah C. Wright and Margaret E. Wright.

CREAMER, lent by Mr. and Mrs. Arnold Gindrat Talbot. Engraved S.A.

SUGAR TONGS, lent by Mr. and Mrs. Arnold Gindrat Talbot. These pieces belonged to Susanna Ashbridge who married John Fairlamb in 1784. Their son, George Fairlamb, married Thomazine Whelen in 1809. Their daughter, Thomazine Fairlamb, married Persifor Frazer Smith in 1833. Their daughter, Rebecca Darlington Smith, married Robert Emmet Monaghan in 1866 and their daughter, Katherine Streeper Monaghan, married Arnold Gindrat Talbot in 1901.

JAMES RIDGEWAY—Boston

b. 1780 d. 1851

SPOON, lent by Mrs. Roy Arthur Hunt. Belonged to the Hunt, McQuesten and Thatcher families and to the Hanchett family of East Douglass, Massachusetts.

GEORGE RIGGS—Baltimore

b. 1777 d. 1864

working dates c. 1805–1810, Georgetown, D. C.

1810–1840, Baltimore

J. Hall Pleasants in his book on "Maryland Silversmiths" says that he was an excellent silversmith, judging from the numerous pieces with his marks and those of Riggs and Griffith which have been preserved. Tea sets by him are well made, attractive in design and substantial in weight, and are not overloaded with repoussé ornament. Riggs used several marks.

WASTE BOWL, lent by Mr. Walter James Steele Buck. This was inherited from the Steeles and Goldsboroughs of Cambridge, Maryland.

DANIEL ROGERS—Newport, Rhode Island

d. 1792

TEASPOON, lent by Mrs. Harrold E. Gillingham.

ANTHONY W. ROBINSON—Philadelphia

working dates 1798–1803

Worked at 23 Strawberry street.

SUGAR TONGS and TWO TEASPOONS, lent by Mrs. John Seaman Albert. They belonged to Mary Keen (born February 3rd, 1766, and died April 16th, 1839) who married November 21st, 1791, John Scudder. She was one of the little girls who scattered flowers before Washington on his visit to Trenton after the Revolutionary War. She was Mr. Albert's great grandmother on his mother's side.

JOEL SAYRE—New York

b. 1778 d. 1818

Born at Southampton, Long Island, November 2, 1778. Later removed to New York where he had a shop at 437 Pearl street in 1802. Died at Cairo, New York, September 28, 1818.

COFFEE SERVICE, four pieces, lent by Mrs. John Seaman
Albert. It belonged to her husband's great grandfather,
John Seaman, of Brooklyn (born 1764 and died De-
cember 19th, 1838) who married Mary Hicks in 1799.

*CREAMER and *SUGAR BOWL, lent by Mrs. W. Clarke
Grieb who gives the history of this silver as follows:

"Isaac Collins, of Burlington, New Jersey, was appointed printer to King George III for the Province of
New Jersey. After revolt of the Colonies he printed
much of the Continental money issued by the Congress.
From his printing office came also, in 1790, the first
quarto Bible printed in America, for which his daughters, Rebecca and Mary, read the proofs.

"As a reward for great accuracy he gave them a sum
of money, with her share of which Mary Collins bought
the cream pitcher and sugar bowl, marked 'M.C.' When
shortly afterward, Mary Collins married Isaac Long-
streth, he had the coffee pot and teapot made to order
to match the cream pitcher and sugar bowl. These two
pieces are marked 'I.M.L.' for Isaac and Mary Long-
streth." Mrs. Grieb is a great granddaughter of Mary
Collins.

THOMAS SHIELDS—Philadelphia

working dates 1765–1794

On July 4th, 1765, Thomas Shields advertised as follows:
"Having opened a shop in Front Street, the third Door
above the Drawbridge, where he has for sale, A neat assortment of Gold, Silver and Jewelry Ware, intends carrying
on his Business in all its Branches and will be greatly
obliged to all Gentlemen and Ladies, that will please to
favour him with their Custom; may depend on having

their Work done in the best and neatest Manner, at the lowest Rates, and with the greatest Despatch."—Pennsylvania Gazette.

In October 31, 1771, he moves, and we find this notice: "Thomas Shields. Acquaints his customers, and the public in general, that he has removed his shop to the 7th house above the Drawbridge, in Front Street, at the Golden Cup and Crown, where he continues carrying on the Goldsmith's business in all its respective branches."—Penna. Gazette.

*CAN, owned by Miss Lydia Fisher Warner. Engraved with the date 1782 and the initials J.S.W. for John and Sarah Warner.

TEA STRAINER, lent by Mrs. William W. Doughten.

*TANKARD, lent by Mr. and Mrs. Christian Febiger. The original owners were Christian Febiger (1746–1796) and his wife, Elizabeth Carson Febiger (1754–1817). See history under Joseph Lownes.

SUGAR BOWL, lent by Mrs. Paul Spencer who says it probably belonged to her great grandfather, Alexander Cook, who was born in Ireland, 1755. He was a member of Captain James Wilson's company in 1776 and also a member of the Home Guard in Philadelphia. He died here in 1839.

GODFREY SHIVING—Philadelphia

working in 1779

PUNCH LADLE, lent by Mrs. Alfred C. Prime.

*CASTOR SET of nine pieces, lent by Mrs. Stanley Eyre Wilson.

JOSEPH SHOEMAKER—Philadelphia

working dates 1793–1839

Philadelphia Directories show him working in Pewter-platter alley in 1793 till 1796.

*CREAMER, lent by Mrs. J. Madison Taylor. It was brought from Charleston, South Carolina, by Colonel William Drayton about 1847.

FOUR TEASPOONS, lent by Miss Gertrude Atkinson. They were part of the wedding silver of her great grandmother, Abigail Woolley, on the occasion of her marriage to her first husband, David Thomas, October 4th, 1814. They were inherited from her grandmother, Elizabeth Justice Thomas Allen, in 1896.

CREAMER, lent by Mrs. Henry Chapman.

FOUR TEASPOONS, lent by Mrs. Walter S. McInnes.

TABLESPOONS, two, lent by Mrs. Walter S. McInnes.

LADLE and TEA SPOON, lent by Mrs. Carroll Williams. Engraved band. Inherited from her ancestors who came from Maryland and Virginia.

TABLESPOONS, lent by Mrs. William Wistar Comfort.

TWO TABLESPOONS, lent by Mrs. Clarence Foster Hand. They are engraved T.H.L. for Thomas and Hannah Laycock.

TEAPOT, lent by Miss Martha Paul Howell. Engraved M.S. to M.S.R. Height 7½ inches and width 12 inches.

ANTHONY SIMMONS—Philadelphia

working dates 1797–1808

Listed in the Philadelphia Directories as working at 27 Race Street, 1799–1808.

Tablespoon, lent by Mrs. Thomas Biddle Ellis. It belonged to her great, great grandfather, John Brientnall Ackley.

J. SNOW—unknown

Gravy Spoon, lent by Mr. and Mrs. Arnold Gindrat Talbot. It belonged to Harriet Taylor who married Joseph Hathaway in 1818.

STODDER AND FROBISHER—Boston

working date 1817

Dessert Spoon, lent by Mr. and Mrs. Arnold Gindrat Talbot. It was originally owned by Louisa Caroline Gindrat who married Richard James Arnold in 1823.

JOHN STOW—Wilmington, Delaware

working in 1772

"Wilmington, November 24, 1772. John Stow begs leave to inform the public, that he has opened a shop in Market-street, next door below Mr. Gabriel Springer's, in Wilmington, where he intends to carry on his business in all its branches; having had peculiar advantages in the large way, such as making coffee-pots, tea-pots, tankards, canns &c. he will undertake any piece of plate that may be wanted; likewise all kinds of small work in gold, silver, plated ditto, jewellery &c. &c. Those who will please to favor him with their custom may depend on having their work well executed."—Pennsylvania Packet, November 30, 1772.

*Tankard, lent by Mrs. Walter M. Jeffords.
Mug, lent by Miss Lydia Wistar Rhoads.
Mug, lent by the Misses Huston.

ROBERT SWAN—Philadelphia

working dates 1799–1831

Worked at 77 south Second street in 1799.

*Coffee Pot and Creamer, lent by Mrs. Joseph Welling-
ton Shannon.   They came to her husband by the will
of an old client who died without heirs.   The story she
told was that they belonged to her parents who had them
made from Mexican dollars.

The family lived at Gettysburg on a large farm and
when the battle was imminent her father's sisters took
the silver and buried it.   In their fright they forgot
where they put it.   The pieces were ploughed up many
years later and were perfectly black.

Teaspoons, two, lent by Miss Sarah Agnes Morison.
They belonged to Mary Cocke Morison, her great grandmother.

THE SYNG FAMILY

PHILIP SYNG, Sr.—Philadelphia and Annapolis

b. 1676 d. 1739   working dates 1720

Philip Syng, Sr., came to Philadelphia from Ireland in
1714 with his wife and three sons.   They were Philip, Jr.,
who became more celebrated as a silversmith than his
father; John, a silversmith also, who died an untimely
death, and Daniel, who went to Lancaster and practiced

his trade of silversmithing there, dying in 1745 when only 32 years of age. Philip, Sr., lived for a time only in Philadelphia. He then went to Cape May, New Jersey, finally moving to Annapolis, Maryland, where he died May 18, 1739, aged 63. Syng has left several important pieces. Among them are the flagon and baptismal basin owned by Christ Church, Philadelphia, and the beautiful silver tray, inkstand and sand shaker in Independence Hall, Philadelphia. The latter were used by the signers of the Declaration of Independence and the Constitution of these United States.

yng, Jr.

PHILIP SYNG, Jr.—Philadelphia

b. 1703 d. 1789   working dates 1738–c. 1772

"Philip Syng, Jr., eldest son of Philip and Abigail (Murdock) born September 29, 1703, probably in County Cork, Ireland, died May 8, 1789, in Philadelphia. Buried in Christ Church. He came to Philadelphia when 11 years old, married February 5, 1729–30, at Christ Church, Elizabeth Warner, daughter of Swen and Esther Warner. He was my ancestor, and his family Bible is in my possession." (This is copied from the account of the Syng Family written by Mr. Alfred Rudulph Justice, since deceased.) On November 28, 1725, when 22 years of age, he embarked for London in the Ship "John," Captain Glentworth. . . . He returned to Philadelphia, June 20, 1726, in the "Yorkshire Grey," Captain James Blythe. (The details are recorded in the family Bible.) While in London Syng made the acquaintance of Benjamin Franklin and their friendship continued throughout their lifetime.

He was a member of Franklin's Junto, and founder with Franklin of the Library Company of Philadelphia. He was one of the directors named in the original Charter, July 1, 1731.

He was a member of the first Masonic Lodge organized in America—called the St. John's Lodge of which Benjamin Franklin was Senior Grand Warden and Philip Syng, Junior Grand Warden. He was one of the founders with Franklin of the University of Pennsylvania and served as trustee till 1773. Philip Syng was also one of the founders of the American Philosophical Society and treasurer of the organization, Benjamin Franklin being President. He was the thirteenth to join the Schuylkill Fishing Company and one of the original members of the Union Fire Company and a Director of the Philadelphia Contributionship for the Insurance of Houses from loss by fire, or the "Hand in Hand," organized in 1752.

Syng was Vestryman of Christ Church and also served as Colonial Treasurer of Philadelphia, 1759–69, and as Provincial Commissioner of Appeals under John Penn. He was the father of eighteen children.

At the Historical Society of Pennsylvania we find in Richard Peter's Account to "The Honourable Proprietaries, July 13, 1750: To cash paid Philip Syng for the County Seal of York £3.14.6. To ditto paid ditto for the County Seal of Cumberland £4.8.0."

The following item is from the Minutes of Common Council of Philadelphia, January 30, 1764, page 696: "An old Account of Philip Syng's against this Board for Medals for Colonel Armstrong for the Punch, Die and Collar, for making the same, amounting to £4.5.6. was exhibited and allowed, and ordered to be paid."

Joseph Richardson, Sr., John Bayley, Philip Syng, Jr., and Edmund Milne made many Indian ornaments of various kinds. In connection with this phase of Colonial Silversmithing Mr. Harrold E. Gillingham has published an interesting article in the Pennsylvania Magazine of History and Biography, Vol. LVIII, April, 1934.

Turning to the newspaper we find that Philip Syng moved to Upper Merion Township in 1772 and that about that time he turned over his business to Richard Humphreys who was one of his journeymen. In the Pennsylvania Gazette for September 23, 1772, we read:

"Richard Humphreys, Goldsmith, Having taken the house in which Philip Syng lately dwelt, hereby informs his friends and the public, that he now carries on the Goldsmith's business in all its branches at the aforesaid place, a few doors below the Coffee-house, where he has for sale, a neat and general assortment of Gold and Silver Ware. . . . Richard Humphreys.

"The subscriber having lately removed into Upper Merion township, hereby informs his friends and former customers, that they may be supplied as usual, at his late dwelling, by the above named Richard Humphreys, whom he hereby recommends to them, as a person qualified to serve them on the best terms, and whose fidelity in the above business will engage their future confidence and regard.—Philip Syng."

On July 21, 1778, Philip Syng inserted the following advertisement in the Pennsylvania Packet: "Stolen last night from the Plantation of Philip Syng, near the ten mile stone, on the Lancaster road, a dark bay Horse . . . One Hundred Dollars reward, or Sixty for the Horse, and reasonable charges on delivery, paid by Thomas Potts, of Pottsgrove, David Potts, of Philadelphia, or Philip Syng, at the Plantation above mentioned."

*Spoons, four, lent by Mr. Robert R. Logan.

*TEA SPOON, lent by Mrs. Harrold E. Gillingham.

*SUGAR NIPPERS, lent by Miss Clarissa T. Chase. Belonged to Sara (Hill) Dillwyn, sister of Margaret (Hill) Morris and great granddaughter of Governor Thomas Lloyd.

*BOWL, lent by Mrs. Raymond Shortlidge.

*SALVER, lent by Mrs. Meredith Hanna and owned by W. Clark Hanna who is the fifth great grandson of the original owner, Rachel Strickland. She was born in 1703 in Dublin, Ireland, daughter of Miles and Frances Strickland who settled in Philadelphia. Rachel married John Hillborn in 1730 and died in this city in 1783, surviving the Revolution.

*CREAMER and *BILL, lent by Mr. Lawrence J. Morris.

COFFEE SPOON, lent by Miss Martha Paul Howell. Engraved on back of handle, I.P.M. 1769.

*COFFEE POT, lent by Mrs. Thomas Evans. Belonged to her great, great grandmother, Mary Benezet.

CAN, lent by Dr. Isaac Starr.

BAPTISMAL BOWL, lent by Mr. Franklin Bache. This bowl was presented to Sarah Franklin, daughter of Benjamin Franklin, by the Reverend David Evans.

*PIE CRUST SALVER and PAIR OF SUGAR TONGS, lent by Mr. and Mrs. C. Jared Ingersoll.

FLUTED PUNCH LADLE, lent by Mrs. Alfred Coxe Prime.

SALVER, lent by Mrs. Ninian Caldwell Cregar. Engraved "E.N. to E.N."

SALVER, lent by Mr. Edward Carey Gardiner.

PORRINGER, lent anonymously. Engraved "F.E.H." It originally belonged to Elizabeth Poultney and Mordecai Lewis Dawson.

*SHELL LADLE, owned by Philip Syng Justice.

JOHN TANGUY—Philadelphia

working dates 1801–1822

In 1818 he worked at 33 North 3rd street.

TWO PITCHERS, lent by Mrs. Charles E. Ingersoll. They were a wedding present to Mrs. Stephen Warren of Troy, New York, from her mother, Mrs. Mabbitt, about 1815.

JOHN AND PETER TARGEE, New York

working date 1811

Located at 192 Water street.

COFFEE POT, CREAMER, SUGAR BOWL, and WASTE BOWL, lent by Mrs. William J. Clothier, who says that her great grandfather, Moses Drake, gave it to his bride, Susanna Morgan as a wedding gift.

TEAPOT and SUGAR BOWL, lent by Miss Anna Warren Ingersoll. It belonged to her great grandmother, Mrs. Stephen Warren, of Troy, New York, and was part of her wedding silver in Lansingburgh in 1808.

WILLIAM THOMSON—New York

working dates 1811–1825

Worked at 399 Broadway. Made a silver service for the Corporation of the City of New York which was presented to Captain Samuel Reid for gallant bravery at the battle of Fayal.

PAP BOWL, lent by Mrs. George M. Marshall who thinks it was a wedding gift to her grandmother's sister whose maiden name was Coit.

B. H. TISDALE—Providence, Rhode Island
working 1824

LADLE WITH SPOUT, lent by Mrs. William Wistar Comfort. Belonged to Mary Hammett Fales.

JACOBUS VANDERSPIEGEL—New York

b. 1668 d. c. 1708   working dates 1701, c. 1705

Captain in the army, 1691. Saw military service along the Albany Frontier when the French invasion was threatening. Appointed Constable of the City in 1698. Registered as goldsmith, 1701, and admitted freeman, 1702.

*PAIR OF TRENCHER SALTS, lent by Mrs. James de W. Cookman, deceased. Courtesy of the Mabel Brady Garvan Collection, Yale. These salts were placed near the trencher or wooden platter on which meat was served; hence, the name.

*TANKARD, lent by Mrs. Horatio Curtis Wood, who tells us the following interesting history: "Its known history begins with the marriage of William Carter and Mary Howell Sutton, widow of Richard Sutton, in Cecil County, Maryland. This took place in 1720, and the initials W.M.C. are on the handle. At the death of Mary Carter the tankard became the property of her daughter, Mary Sutton, who in 1734 married John Morris, son of Anthony and Phoebe Guest Morris. They brought the tankard to Philadelphia. It was next owned by William Morris, then by Dr. John Morris, and then by his daughter, Margaret, who in 1810 married Isaac Colins, Jr., son of Isaac Collins, printer at Burlington. He published the Collins Bible, one of the earliest American Bibles, and also printed Colonial currency for

New Jersey. Their son, William Morris Collins, was given the tankard because his initials were W.M.C. and through his daughter, Lydia Cope Collins, who married John Bacon Wood, it came to her oldest son, the present owner, Horatio Curtis Wood. The initials in script on the lid, W.W.S., have not been identified. Perhaps the first owner placed them there but the history of the first twenty years of the tankard is lost in the fogs of the past."

This is, so far, the seventh Vanderspiegel tankard known.

DANIEL VAN VOORHIS—Philadelphia and New York
working dates 1779–1798

We read in the Pennsylvania Journal for April 24, 1782, that "Daniel Van Voorhis Informs the Public, that he has removed from his late Dwelling-house in Market street, to the west side of Front-street, six doors below the Coffee-house where he continues to carry on the business in all its branches." He advertises in the New Jersey Gazette on December 4, 1782: "Having removed from Philadelphia, takes this method to inform his friends in particular, and the publick in general, that he has now opened shop in Princeton, a small distance to the eastward of the college, where he intends, &. . . . " In 1785 he was located in New York. He worked at 141 Broadway in 1797.

*Base of Sugar Urn or Goblet, lent by Mrs. Charles W. Perkins.

JOHN VERNON—New York
working dates 1787–1815

Advertised at 41 Water street in 1793 and at 75 Gold

street in 1815. The following piece is attributed to John Vernon.

*SUGAR BOWL, urn shaped, lent by Mrs. Roland B. Whitridge.

SAMUEL VERNON—Newport, Rhode Island

b. 1683   working dates 1714–37

Born in Newport, December 6, 1683. Registered as a freeman in 1714. Shortly after his second marriage he was appointed by the Assembly to settle a controversy concerning some grants of land. He was one of the most prominent silversmiths of that period.

*PORRINGER, owned by the family of the late William Rotch Wister. It has a geometric handle and is engraved E.W.M.B. "E.W." is for Elizabeth Wanton, born January 5th, 1691, and married Abraham Borden, 1713. He was the son of Matthew Borden (born in 1638) the first white child to be born on the island of what is now Rhode Island. The "M.B." stands for her daughter, Mary Borden, born May, 1729. She married, in 1750, Thomas Rodman, of Newport. They were the parents of Samuel Rodman of New Bedford, who married Elizabeth Rotch, daughter of William Rotch, Sr., and Elizabeth Barney, of Nantucket and New Bedford. Samuel and Elizabeth Rotch Rodman were the parents of Mary Rodman who married in 1805 William Logan Fisher of "Wakefield," Bristol Township, Philadelphia County. William Logan and Mary Rodman Fisher were the parents of Sarah Logan Fisher, born 1806 and married in 1826, William Wister of "Vernon," Germantown. Wil-

liam and Sarah Logan (Fisher) Wister were the parents
of the late William Rotch Wister in whose family the
porringer now belongs.

*Pepper Pot, lent by Mrs. William Wistar Comfort.   En-
graved M.E.F. for Mary Engs Fales.

*Spoon with Rat Tail, lent by Mrs. Arnold Gindrat
Talbot.   This spoon is engraved F.W. to A.C.   Belonged to a Wheeler ancestor of Saulesburry, Massachusetts.

WILLIAM VILANT—Philadelphia

working date 1725

*Tankard, lent by Dr. George Morrison Coates.   It be-
longed to his third great grandfather.

Two Spoons, lent by Mr. Robert R. Logan.

Tankard, anonymous loan.

*Tankard, lent by The Philadelphia Museum of Art.

JOHN WAITE—Kingston, Rhode Island

b. 1742 d. 1817   working date 1767

" 'On April 13, 1769, Jorn Waite . . . Silversmith of
South Kingston' purchased from Elisha Reynolds, 'one
Quarter of an acre . . . with a Dwelling House thereon
standing.'   This house and land were situated on the
South side of the highway leading to the Westward through
the village of Little Rest and nearly opposite to the present
post office.   It was in the basement of this old house that
Waite worked and here he had his shop until the time of
his death."—Quoted from "The Silversmiths of Little
Rest" by Wm. D. Miller.

*TABLESPOONS, lent by Mrs. William Wistar Comfort. Marked P.V. for Patty Varnum, wife of General James Varnum, who was Aide to George Washington. At one time he was quartered near Valley Forge.

JOHN WARD—Philadelphia
working dates 1810–11

TEA POT, anonymous loan.
*SUGAR TONGS, lent by Mrs. John Madison Taylor. They were brought from Charleston, South Carolina, by Colonel William Drayton in 1814.

WARD AND BARTHOLOMEW—Hartford, Connecticut
working dates 1804–1809

CREAMER, lent by Mrs. H. Norris Harrison.

T. & A. E. WARNER—Baltimore
working dates 1805–1812

Thomas and Andrew Ellicott Warner worked at 5 Gay street.

LADLE, lent by Mrs. Thornton Oakley. Belonged to Eliza Moylan Lansdale, daughter of General Stephen Moylan.

EDWARD WATSON—Boston
working dates 1821–1839

TWO FORKS, lent by Mr. Edward Carey Gardiner.

JAMES WATSON—Philadelphia

working dates 1820–1850

Had his shop at 72 High street.

MUSTARD SPOON, lent by Mrs. A. Sydney Logan, deceased.

EMMOR T. WEAVER—Philadelphia

b. 1786 d. 1860   working dates 1808–1833

Listed as a silversmith and swordmaker, worked in 1820 at 20 North 4th street, and 1 Loxleys court.

TWO TEASPOONS, lent by Mrs. William S. Freeman.
LADLE, lent by Mrs. Meredith Hanna.

JOSHUA WEAVER—West Chester, Pennsylvania

b. 1753 d. 1827   working dates 1794–1808

TWO TEASPOONS, lent by Mrs. William S. Freeman. They belonged to her mother whose family had always lived in or near West Chester.

A. G. WELLES—Boston

working c. 1804

TWO TEA POTS, lent by Mrs. Henry A. Berwind, Jr.
CREAMER, lent by Mrs. Henry Percival Glendinning.
SUGAR BOWL, lent by Mrs. Logan M. Bullitt. These pieces are all of the same set, and belonged to John Langdon Frothingham, Ephram Langdon Frothingham and Mary Frothingham Roberts. Mrs. Glendinning, Mrs. Bullitt and Mrs. Berwind, Jr., are the fourth generation to own these pieces.

BERNARD WENMAN—New York

working dates 1789–1805

Two Teaspoons, lent by Mrs. Harrold E. Gillingham.

WHARTENBY AND BUMM—Philadelphia

working dates 1816, 1818

*Wine Cooler, lent by the Historical Society of Pennsylvania.

SAMUEL WILLIAMSON—Philadelphia

working dates 1794, 1813

Worked at 70 south Front street in 1794–96, at 118 south Front street in 1811.

Two Spoons, lent by Mrs. Harrold E. Gillingham.
Coffee Pot and Teapot, lent by The Misses Ashbridge.
Coffee Pot, lent by Mrs. Walter Penn Shipley.
Teaspoon, lent by Mrs. James A. G. Campbell.

R. & W. WILSON—Philadelphia

working dates 1825, 1846

Creamer and Sugar Bowl, lent by Mrs. Elisha Crowell, deceased. Now owned by Miss Frances Kimball Crowell.
Vegetable Dish, lent by Mr. Edward Carey Gardiner.

CHRISTIAN WILTBERGER—Philadelphia

b. 1766 d. 1851   working dates 1793, 1817

In 1797 we find Mr. Wiltberger inserting the following advertisement in the Aurora (Philadelphia) : "Silver-smith and Jeweller, Informs his Friends and the Public, that he has removed from No. 33 South Second-Street to No. 13, North Second-Street, nearly opposite Christ Church, where he continues to carry on the Silver Smith and Jeweller's business in all its branches as usual."   In the Directory for 1793 he lists himself as a "Goldsmith, jeweller and hairworker."   Christian Wiltberger produced silver of a high quality, many of his sugar urns having the delicate "gallery" which is seldom seen excepting in Philadelphia made silver.

CREAMER, lent by Mrs. Thomas Evans.

SUGAR BOWL, lent by Mr. Barry Hepburn.

WASTE BOWL, lent by The Misses Huston.

TWO TEASPOONS, lent by Mrs. Henry D. Paxson, deceased.

TWO DESSERT SPOONS, lent by Mrs. Alfred C. Prime. Bright cutting. Family pieces with bird on back of bowl.

TWO TABLESPOONS, lent by Mrs. Alfred C. Prime. Bright cutting.   Family pieces with bird on back of bowl.

TWO DESSERT SPOONS, lent by The Misses Hannah C. and Margaret E. Wright.

TEASPOON, lent by Mrs. George T. Lukens, who says it is one of a set of a dozen.   They were the wedding silver of Joseph and Anne Callender Price who married 5 mo. 5th, 1790.   The spoons are marked on the front "J.A.P." and on the back, "married 1790."   They belonged to Mrs. Lukens' great, great grandparents.

TABLESPOONS and SUGAR TONGS, lent by Mrs. Walter S. McInnes.

COFFEE POT and TWO TABLESPOONS, lent by Mrs. Richard Waln Miers.   Marked S.R. for Sarah Ridgeway (born 1779 and died 1872).   She married on April 11,

1799, Nicholas Waln of Walnford, New Jersey. She was the great grandmother of Mr. Miers.

*SUGAR URN, lent by Mrs. Daniel M. Shewbrooks.

*BOWL, lent by Mrs. Alfred Stengel.

EDWARD WINSLOW—Boston

1669, 1753

He was one of the greatest of the Colonial silversmiths. He married three times. In 1669 he was appointed Constable. Granted permit to open a shop as a goldsmith in 1702. Appointed Captain of Artillery Company in 1714. He was elected Sheriff of Suffolk County in 1728–43. Lost two of his sons at Louisburg in 1745. Served as Colonel in the Boston Regiment in 1733. Chosen Judge of the inferior Court of Common Pleas.

*PORRINGER, lent by Mrs. William Wistar Comfort. Inscribed underneath "Mary Chapman's legacy to Mary Gold."

CHILD'S CUP, lent anonymously.

BANCROFT WOODCOCK—Wilmington, Delaware

working dates 1754, 1772

In the Pennsylvania Packet for July 4th, 1754, we find the following: "Bancroft Woodcock, Goldsmith, Hereby informs the publick, that he has set up his business in Wilmington near the upper Market house, where all persons that please to favor him with their custom, may be supplied with all sorts of Gold and silver work, after the neatest and newest fashions. N.B. Said Woodcock gives the full value for old gold and silver."—April 13, 1772, Penna. Packet.

Again in 1772, we find a house for sale, "situate in Market-street, in the borough of Wilmington . . . nearly opposite the shop of Bancroft Woodcock, Silversmith. . . . N.B. Said Woodcock continues to finish his work in the neatest manner, as usual, and gives the best prices for old gold and silver."

*Sugar Urn with Lid, lent by the Philadelphia Museum of Art. This was once owned by James Smith, a signer of the Declaration of Independence.

Two Spoons, lent by Miss Lydia Wistar Rhoads.

*Can, lent by Mr. Lardner Howell. It was a wedding present to Mary Whitlock Dawes who married Samuel Emelen Howell in 1798, grandparents of Mrs. Howell.

ENGLISH, IRISH, FOREIGN AND UNIDENTIFIED SILVER

English Silver

*1675, London—CAUDLE CUP, lent by Mrs. Evan Randolph. This piece was probably made by John Sutton and has a flat chased and embossed design of a dog chasing a rabbit amid a floral pattern on the bowl. It was brought to this country in 1688 by Henry and Lydia Armitage Hollingsworth, the great, great, great, great grandparents of the present owner.

SPOON, lent by Mrs. Mantle Fielding, whose early ancestor, Mark Reeve, brought it from England in the ship "Griffin" in 1676. The hall marks are almost obliterated but the type is very early.

*c. 1690—SPOON, lent by Mrs. Harrold Edgar Gillingham. Rat tail and trifid end.

*1698—Two SPOONS, lent by Miss Lydia Wistar Rhoads. John Ladyman made these rat tail spoons with the trifid ends. They are engraved "B.S.W." for Bartholomew (died 1726) and Sarah (Ashton) Wyatt whose granddaughter, Sarah Wyatt, married Richard Wistar, son of immigrant, Caspar Wistar, and so descended to Miss Rhoads.

1700–1718, Chester, England—COFFEE POT, lent by Mrs. B. Brannan Reath, II. This piece is Britianna silver, the fine standard.

1700–1720—*POMANDER, lent by Mrs. Alfred Coxe Prime. The word pomander is a corruption of the old French phrase, "pomme d'ambre," meaning apple of amber. This was ambergris, a waxy substance coming

from the sperm whale which when slightly warmed diffused a pleasant perfume.   A small ball of ambergris or
or of musk enclosed in a silver container was sometimes
worn on a chain around the neck or hung from the
girdle to counteract fevers and also the many offensive
smells prevailing in the Middle Ages.   There is a pomander much like this one in the Boston Museum of
Fine Arts and another in the Philadelphia Museum of
Art.

*c. 1709—SPOON, lent by Mrs. Harrold Edgar Gillingham.
Rat tail and trifid end.

1713, London—CHILD'S CAUDLE CUP, lent by Mrs. William Hill Steeble.   This cup has come down in the West
and Maris families.

1714—MUG, lent by Miss Susanna Wright.   This piece
was brought from England by another Susanna Wright.
She was seventeen years old at the time.   She was the
first person to bring silk worms to this country and to
make silk.   A piece of the latter she sent to Queen
Anne who sent her a handsome portfolio which is owned
by Miss Hannah C. Wright and Miss Margaret E.
Wright.   The Wright arms are on the mug.

1721—PINT CAN, lent by Dr. George Morrison Coates
who inherited it from his fifth great grandfather.

1723—BOWL WITH COVER, lent by Mrs. David Chandler
Prince.   There is the Atkins coat of arms on the bowl
and the owner has written the history as follows: "Mrs.
David Chandler Prince received it in 1919 from her
mother, Katharine Parker Howard Notman.   It was
a gift from Miss Julia Soule, of Portland, Maine, a first
cousin of Mrs. Notman's mother, Pamela Atkins Colman Howard.

"Mrs. Notman and Miss Soule were lineal descendants

of Capt. Joseph Atkins (1680–1773) and his son, William (1711–1788), through Susanna Atkins (1762–1827), the daughter of William Atkins, who married Dr. Samuel Colman, of Newburyport, Massachusetts.

"Captain Joseph Atkins and his son, William, settled in Newbury, Massachusetts, prior to 1722. Captain Atkins had been at sea since his boyhood in Sandwich, Kent, England, and had engaged in coastwise trade before settling down in Newbury."

1724, London—CAN, lent by Mr. Robert R. Logan. The maker is Joseph Clare.

*1724—SALVER, lent by Mr. Robert R. Logan.

1730—CREAMER, lent by Mr. Robert R. Logan.

*1731, London—BRANDY WARMER, lent by Mrs. Alfred Coxe Prime.

1732, London—TANKARD, lent by Mrs. Thornton Oakley. The tankard was made by Thomas Parr and belonged to Mrs. Oakley's great, great grandfather, James Hunter, who was born in Scotland in 1729 and died in Philadelphia in 1796. (See complete history under Edmund Milne, brandy warmer.)

1735—SPOON, lent by Mrs. Henry B. Robb.

*1741—SALVER, lent by Mrs. Alfred Stengel. The maker is Joseph Sanders.

1754, London—CAN, lent by Mrs. Thomas Evans. At present it is on exhibition at the Philadelphia Museum of Art. Mrs. Evans says that the original owner was her great, great grandmother, Mary Benezet.

1748—Two SALVERS, lent by Mrs. Alfred Coxe Prime. Both have Mary Searle scratched on the back. One was made by Thomas Parr and is hall marked 1748. It also has the cypher M.S. on it. The other has no marks at all, but has the monogram, J.M.S., for John and Mary

Searle. Their history is as follows: Mary Hicks married
John Searle. Their daughter, Mary Searle, married John
Barclay, December 11th, 1781. John Barclay was
mayor of Philadelphia in 1791 and a signer of the ratification of the Constitution from Bucks County, Pennsylvania. Their daughter, Mary Searle Barclay, married
Clement Cornell Biddle, March 10th, 1814. Their son,
John Barclay Biddle, married Caroline Phillips, November 7th, 1850. Their daughter, Anna Clifford Biddle,
married Clement Stocker Phillips, November 15th,
1881. Their daughter, Phoebe Caroline Phillips, the
present owner, married Alfred Coxe Prime, June 14th,
1922.

1749, London—PORRINGER, lent by Mrs. Thomas Evans
and now exhibited at the Philadelphia Museum of Art.
It was made by William Shaw and belonged to her great,
great grandmother, Mary Benezet.

1750, London—*TEAPOT and *SUGAR BOWL, lent by Mrs.
Meredith Hanna and made by Richard Gurney & Company. These pieces were originally owned by Rachel
Strickland who married John Hillborn in Philadelphia
in 1730. They descended to her daughter and granddaughter, Rachel Roberts Jones Wiltbank, bearing the
name of Rachel. Mary Elizabeth Wiltbank, daughter
of Rachel Wiltbank, married W. Goodell Clark and
their daughter, Marion Wiltbank Clark is the great,
great, great, great granddaughter of the original owner
and the present owner of the silver.

1750–52—*KETTLE, *STAND, and *SALVER, lent by Miss
Alice M. Prime. The kettle was made by George
Wickes in 1752. The stand is dated 1750–1 and the
salver, 1744. This beautiful set was a presentation piece
to John Clements, Mayor of Bristol, on New Year's

Day, 1753, by the Sheriffs of that city, this being the custom every year. The four coats of arms on the salver are as follows: upper left, arms of the City of Bristol; upper right, Clements arms; lower left, arms of Daniel Woodward; lower right, arms of Edward Whatley. These last two were the Sheriffs who presented the kettle to John Clements. It was brought to America by Sarah Clement Stocker, or her son, Anthony Stocker, who settled in Philadelphia. Anthony Stocker was married here, November 14, 1754, to Margaret Phillips. Miss Prime is sixth in descent from John and Sarah (Clement) Stocker.

*1752—TANKARD, lent by Miss Lydia Fisher Warner and made by William Grundy. Engraved 1782, J.S.W. It was probably the wedding silver of John and Sarah Warner.

1754, London—SAUCEBOAT, lent by Mrs. William Wistar Comfort. It is engraved M.M.F. for Mary Magdalen Flagg, of Charleston, S. C.

1755, London—*PAIR OF SALT CELLARS and SPOONS, lent by Mrs. W. Goodell Clark and made by William Plummer. The original owner was Mrs. Clark's great, great, great grandmother, Rachel Strickland, who came from Dublin, Ireland, and married John Hillborn in Philadelphia in 1730.

* 1760-1—SALVER, lent by Mrs. Edwin Schenck. It was made by Robert Rew. Belonged to Charles Carroll of Carrollton.

1761—PAIR OF SALT CELLARS, lent by Mr. Robert R. Logan.

1762—PAIR OF SALT CELLARS, lent by Mrs. Albert Atlee Jackson, who says that the salt cellars are engraved with the block letters, A. and E.T.B., which stand for her great, great, great grandfather, Abraham Ten Broeck (1734–1810), and Elizabeth Van Rensselaer. Abraham Ten Broeck was at one time a member of the House of Assembly under the Colonial Government for the Manor of Rensselaerwyck and after the Revolution became a member of the Provincial Congress of New York. He was a Brigadier General during the Revolutionary War and was an "intimate and beloved friend of General Washington and was selected by him as his special companion on several important expeditions." When the British evacuated New York he was one of the Council appointed to receive possession. He was a New York State Senator and President of the Convention that adopted its first Constitution. He became the first President of the bank of Albany and was elected Mayor of Albany from 1779–1783 and from 1796–1799.

*1763, London—PAIR OF CANDLESTICKS, lent by Mrs. Addinell Hewson and made by Louis Black. They are engraved with the inscription: "The gift of Benjamin Franklin, L.L.D.—F.R.S." Mrs. Hewson explains that the candlesticks were a wedding gift from Benjamin Franklin to Mary Stevenson who married Dr. William Hewson, a surgeon and anatomist of London, in 1770. They were inherited by her son, Dr. Thomas Hewson, who bequeathed them to Dr. Addinell Hewson and thence to her husband, named for his father.

1763—TANKARD, lent by Mrs. John Hampton Barnes. Thomas Wipham and Charles Wright are the makers.

1763—TRAY, lent by Mr. Walter James Steele Buck and made by Robert Rew. It belonged to Mr. Buck's mother who inherited it from her ancestors, the Steeles and Goldboroughs, on the Eastern Shore of Maryland.

1764—SALVER, lent by Mrs. Edward Wanton Smith and made by Hannam & Mills.

*1764—TRAY, lent by Mrs. Francis von A. Cabeen, and made by Thomas Hannam and Richard Mills. The original owner was Jacob Barge.

*1771, London—SMALL SALVER, lent by Mrs. Alfred Coxe Prime. This piece made by John Carter is a stand for a teapot.

1772—SALVER, lent by the family of William Rotch Wister. Engraved "S.L." Wedding silver of Sarah Logan (born, November 6, 1751—died, January 25, 1796). She was the daughter of William Logan of Stenton who was the son of James Logan, Secretary to William Penn. Her mother was Sarah Read. Sarah Logan married, March 17, 1772, Thomas Fisher, son of Joshua and Sarah (Roland) Fisher. The salver was inherited by their son, William Logan Fisher (1781–1862) of "Wakefield," Bristol Township, Philadelphia County, Pennsylvania, who married Mary Rodman (1781–1813) of New Bedford, Massachusetts. Their daughter, Sarah Logan Fisher (1806–1891), married, in 1826, William Wister of "Vernon," Germantown, Pennsylvania. Their son, the late William Rotch Wister (1827–1911), married in 1868, Mary Rebecca Eustis, daughter of Frederic Augustus and Mary Channing Eustis, of Milton, Massachusetts.

1773—Made in Sheffield, *KNIVES AND FORKS, lent by Mrs. Andrew Wright Crawford. Richard Tudor made this set of eight dinner knives and forks. Mrs. Crawford tells us: "They have been continuously in the possession of my mother's family since 1773 and were used by my grandmother, Sarah Ann Gorham F. Randolph, wife of James Clark, D.D. Originally they were the property of my great, great, great grandfather, Joseph F. Randolph, 3d (1722–1782), who married Esther Broderick about 1742. Joseph F. Randolph, 3d, was the great grandson of Edward F. Randolph, who emigrated in 1630 from Nottinghamshire, England, to Massachusetts. He married on May 10, 1637, Elizabeth, born at Leyden, Holland, in 1620, a daughter of Thomas and Anne Blossom of Barnstable, who were among the first Pilgrim settlers of New England. Edward F. Randolph was said to be a direct descendant of Rolf, the Norsman, who conquered Normandy in the year 912 A. D."

1773—SALVER, lent by Mrs. B. Brannen Reath, 2nd, made by Robert Rogers.

*1774—CREAMER, lent by Mrs. Alfred Coxe Prime. The marks are partially obliterated but the date letter is 1774.

1774—*CREAMER, lent by Mrs. Alfred Coxe Prime. It is inverted pear shaped with gadrooned edge on the splay base. Engraved J.H.K. It belonged to John Henry Kepple who married, in 1741, Anna Catherine Barbara Bauer. (He died in 1797.) Their daughter, Catherine Maria Kepple, married John Steinmetz on April 18, 1765. Their daughter, Sarah Frederica Salome Steinmetz, married John Hill Brinton on April 30, 1795. Their daughter, Mary Brinton, married Clements Stocker Phillips, October 25, 1838. Their son, Clement Stocker Phillips, married Anna Clifford Biddle, November 15, 1881. Their daughter, Phoebe Caroline Phillips, married Alfred Coxe Prime, June 14, 1922. She is the present owner.

1774—FOUR SPOONS, lent by Miss Sarah Agnes Morison and made by Hester Bateman. The spoons which have a crest belonged to Mary Chapman, great grandmother of Miss Morison.

1774—SUGAR TONGS, lent by Mrs. Harrold Edgar Gillingham. The tongs are also made by Hester Bateman.

1775–6—Made in Sheffield, *Teapot, lent by Mrs. Alfred Stengel. The maker is J. Rowbotham.

1783—Oyster Ladle, lent by Miss Clarissa T. Chase who explains: "It is engraved with the Hill crest and belonged to Deborah Moore Hill, wife of Richard Hill, Mayor of Philadelphia, and granddaughter of Governor Thomas Lloyd. I am eighth in descent of Governor Thomas Lloyd."

1783—Soup Tureen, lent by Mrs. T. Wistar Brown.

*Spoon—unidentified, lent by Mrs. William Wistar Comfort.

Sugar Tongs, date and maker unknown—lent by Mr. Daniel Wister, deceased. Original owners, Daniel and Lowrey Wister who married in 1760.

Boatswain's Whistle and Coffee Pot, date and maker unknown—lent by Mrs. Winthrop Sargent and property of Gorham P. Sargent. These pieces were taken from a British vessel captured and brought into Gloucester Harbor during the Revolution as a prize by the "General Stark" which was owned by Mrs. Sargent's great, great grandfather, Winthrop Sargent. There is the coat of arms of the English owner on one side of the coffee pot and the Sargent arms on the other.

Muffinier, unidentified, lent by Mrs. William P. Hacker. It originally belonged to Samuel Morris, First Captain of the Philadelphia City Troop (1734–1812). He married Rebecca Wistar (1735/36–1791) at Christ Church, Philadelphia, in 1755. The muffinier is engraved "S. R.M." It came to William Platt Hacker from his uncle, Caspar Wistar Hacker, who inherited it from his aunt, Elizabeth Hacker, who in turn received it from her aunt, Katherine Brown. The piece originally came from Cedar Grove now in Fairmount Park, Philadelphia.

Irish Silver

1783—SUGAR TONGS, made in Dublin by Michael Keating, lent by Mrs. Ninian Caldwell Cregar. Engraved C.M. F. for Charles and Margaret Ferris. Charles Ferris was born in 1767. This piece belongs to his great, great, great granddaughter, Mary Rebecca Cregar.

1756—TWO TABLESPOONS—John Bolland, maker, lent by Mr. Henry Paul Busch. Two items are quoted from the will of Sarah Ash, dated, July 28, 1785. "Item—I give and bequeath unto my Granddaughter, Sarah Fort, one silver tablespoon. Item—I give and bequeath unto my granddaughter, Mary Fort, one silver tablespoon." Sarah and Mary were sisters. Sarah did not marry. Her spoon later returned to Mary who married Amos Palmer. Their daughter, Mary, married Miers Busch. The spoons passed on to their son, Henry E. Busch, and to his son, Henry Paul Busch.

Foreign Silver

French, c. 1820—CHOCOLATE POT, lent by Mrs. Frederick Fraley. Belonged to Helen Fisher and Charles S. Bradford.

French—VEGETABLE DISH WITH LID, lent by Mrs. John Hampton Barnes. Believed to have been in America before 1776.

*SALVER, believed to be French, owned by Mr. May Stevenson Easby, engraved with coat of arms and the letters P.E.H.

*CAKE BASKET, owned by Mr. May Stevenson Easby, 18th century. Made in Amsterdam or Brussels. This piece has a series of names and dates engraved on the back as follows: "John Phillips, died September 22nd, 1762. To his son, John Phillips, died April 27, 1806. William

Phillips, died August 24, 1845. To his son, John S. Phillips, died March 24, 1876. To his sister, Anna Phillips Stevenson, died February 15, 1894. To her daughter, Rebecca Phillips Mason. To her sister, Elizabeth Clifford Easby, died January 18, 1935. To her son, May Stevenson Easby. To his son, George Gordon Meade Easby."

The William Phillips, one time owner of this basket, had an interesting history, part of which is quoted here. He was elected to membership in the First Troop Philadelphia City Cavalry (the 156th member on their rolls) September 12th, 1794. He resigned, October 2nd, 1809. During his enlistment in the Troop he took part in the Whiskey Insurrection in Western Pennsylvania from September 16th, 1794, till December 13th, 1794. (From the Troop history.)

There is another story about William Phillips which, even in this day and generation makes interesting reading. It is copied as follows from a letter from David Lewis, December, 1880, written to Camilla Conner, afterward Mrs. Arthur Hale: "Somewhere about 1794–5 Mr. Phillips, having finished his mercantile education in the counting house of George Meade, grandfather of General Meade, loaded two ships and sailed for Bordeaux. . . . He then proceeded to London, in order to sell his cargoes to the Admiralty in which he succeeded. While in London he boarded in a house with several other young Americans, among whom were Mr. Daniel W. Coxe of this city, Mr. Tabb and some other Virginians, quite ready for a lark. One of the most enterprising had an idea and as the rest seemed destitute of that rare thing, they seized upon his, which was to go to Court, after the newly invented equality fashion without submitting to the aristocratic formality of a presentation. The party went on the first occasion which I suspect was the "Queen's drawing room." They did not carry their republican principles, however, to go "sans culottes" but condescended to hire from the Noses & Sons of that day second-hand court suits and swords, probably ornamented with large glass jewels, at an expense of a guinea apiece for that night only. In this glittering garb they were conveyed in sedan chairs to the entrance and fell into line with the courtiers. I do not remember the number of the party and only the name of one other, Mr. Daniel W. Coxe. They passed in the ring without any notice, but lingering in the room the Queen observed with Royal quickness of eye that they were something new and strange and sent a page to investigate the Yankee Nation, then in its extreme youth. They took the hint and vanished but were not deterred from returning to the ball that followed that night. This was held in a place said by Mr. Phillips to have been very like St. Peters Church with its gallery on three sides. He was admitted to the gallery and from there observed the progress of the ball. The King and Queen (King George III and Queen Charlotte) entered with their attendants and took their seats or rather thrones under a canopy and then the Royal Family followed in pairs and arranged themselves on each hand of their parents. To understand this proceeding or rather procession it must be remembered that at that time the Royal Pair had their quiver full of fifteen, the youngest was 13. In addition was the young Duke of Gloucester, their cousin, who afterwards married the Princess Mary. This young Prince seemed to Mr. Phillips the most enviable of men from his position and appearance. The

ball was opened by the Prince of Wales dancing a minuet
with his elder sister followed by the Duke of Gloucester
and the other Dukes of the troupe which was executed
with great beauty and grace as you might have expected
from the First gentlemen in Europe.   In the meantime
Mr. Phillips was seated in the gallery and next to him sat
a gentleman who entered into conversation with him,
and seeing he was a stranger very politely told him he
would be glad to give him the names of any persons in
the Court that he did not know.   A gentleman hap-
pening to enter the ball room at that time Mr. Phillips
enquired who he was when his new friend told him:
"That is Mr. Pitt," and observed that he must have been
in London a very short time not to have known him,
and then went on to ask him his own country.   Mr.
Phillips told him he was from Philadelphia, when his new
acquaintance seemed to be interested and told him that
he had been in Philadelphia some years ago and knew a
great many persons there.   He enquired about many
of the ladies and among others was very particular in
asking about the Miss Chews of whom Mr. Phillips gave
him every information.   His enquiring friend turned
out to be Sir William Howe who commanded the British
troops occupying Philadelphia in 1777."

LARGE SPOON WITH FOREIGN MARKS—date and maker
unknown, lent by Mr. and Mrs. Arnold Gindrat Talbot.

Unidentified and Unmarked Silver

These pieces are listed alphabetically according to the
owners.

SPOON, belonged to Christoffle and Ruth Cowart Stryker.
Lent by Mrs. John Seaman Albert.

FOUR SPOONS, belonged to great grandfather, William
Randolph (1794–1861), of Woodbridge, N. J.   They

were made from his knee buckles and marked "C.G."
Lent by Mrs. John Seaman Albert.

NUTMEG GRATER, unmarked.

WASTE BOWL, unmarked.
Lent by Mrs. Edgar Wright Baird.

*MOTE SPOON, unidentified. These small spoons were used to take tea leaves from the tea cup. They are perforated with beautiful designs.

*NUTMEG GRATER, unidentified.
Lent by Mrs. Francis von A. Cabeen.

NUTMEG GRATERS, unidentified.

PAIR OF SALT CELLARS, unidentified.
Lent by Mrs. Hampton L. Carson, deceased.

NUTMEG GRATER, unidentified. American.

SNUFF BOX, unidentified.

SNUFF BOX, unidentified. American, 1765.

SUGAR TONGS, unidentified. American.
Lent by Mr. Joseph Carson.

CREAMER, 18th Century, unidentified. Belonged to Philip Brown Chase.

SIX TEASPOONS, unidentified. Engraved "C."

*DOLL'S SUGAR BOWL, marked R.P. Belonged to Margaret (Hill) Morris, great granddaughter of Governor Thomas Lloyd.
Lent by Miss Clarissa T. Chase.

TEAPOT, unidentified. Belonged to her great, great, great grandfather, James Lynah, M.D., (1737–1809) who removed the bullet from General Pulaski at the siege of Savannah, Georgia.
Lent by Mrs. Samuel Hart Chase.

SUGAR BOWL, unmarked.
Lent by Mrs. Edward Walter Clark, deceased.

KNEE BUCKLES, unidentified, belonged to David Fales, 1727.

KNIVES, unmarked, with feather edge.   Belonged to Dr. Peter Turner, Revolutionary surgeon.

TABLESPOONS, marked "I.M." and engraved J.R.H.

TEASPOONS, unmarked.   Engraved "E.T." for Elizabeth Turner, c. 1745.

Lent by Mrs. William Wistar Comfort.

WINE STRAINER, unmarked.

Lent by Mrs. James de W. Cookman, deceased.

CREAMER, unidentified, 1787.

Lent by Mr. and Mrs. R. P. Cookman.

WASTE BOWL, marked W. W.

Lent by Mr. and Mrs. Rodney P. Cookman.

SNUFF BOX, unidentified and inlaid with gold.   Belonged to Thomas Waring who gave it to his son, Charles Robinson Waring, the owner's great grandfather, for whom it is engraved.   It came from England with Thomas Waring about 1790.

Lent by Mrs. Henry Erdman.

SUGAR TONGS, American, unidentified.

Lent by Mrs. William S. Freeman.

PUNCH LADLE, 1754, unidentified.

TWO TABLESPOONS, unidentified.

Lent by Mr. Edward Carey Gardiner.

*BABY'S NURSING NIPPLE WITH BOTTLE, unidentified, American, c. 1815.

FILLING SPOON, marked W.G. and engraved W.H.H. in oval.

*FUNNEL, unidentified.

INVALID'S FEEDING TUBE, marked W.P.J.P., American, c. 1800.

NIPPLE, unidentified.

PAP CUP, marked T.C., American, c. 1770.

SPOON, marked G.M., American, c. 1710.   Rat tail with trifid end.

TEASPOON, marked A.B., American, c. 1760.

TEASPOON, marked B.T., c. 1740.

TWO TEASPOONS, marked A. Scott.

TWO TODDY SPOONS, unidentified, c. 1790.

*TONGUE SCRAPER, unidentified, American, c. 1775.

> Lent by Mrs. Harrold Edgar Gillingham.

SPOON, no maker's mark. Belonged to Unicem Swain, 1744, and inherited by Virginia Roberts Glendinning in 1904, her great, great, great granddaughter.

> Lent by Mrs. Henry P. Glendinning.

*STRAINER, unidentified. Engraved S.S.H. for Samuel (1723–1807) and Sarah (Stretch) Howell who were married in 1745. Inherited by the fifth generation.

> Lent by Mrs. Joseph B. Hutchinson.

CREAMER, unidentified.

> Lent by Miss Anna Warren Ingersoll.

PORRINGER, unidentified.

> Lent by Mr. and Mrs. C. Jared Ingersoll.

WASTE BOWL, unidentified, c. 1781.

> Lent by Mrs. Charles E. Ingersoll.

TEAPOT, marked I.L. & A.S.

SMALL SALVER with pie-crust, marked I.L. & A.S.

> Lent by Mrs. William Norton Johnson.

TWO COFFEE POTS and TWO PITCHERS, unidentified. 1820.

> Lent by Mrs. Charles M. Lea.

SPOON, unmarked.

FOUR TEASPOONS, unmarked. Belonged to Mary Morris Griffiths, wife of Thomas Griffiths, Provincial Counsellor, 1717.

> Lent by Mrs. A. Sidney Logan, deceased.

SMALL SPOON, marked P.S.

> Lent by Mrs. Walter S. McInnes.

SUGAR BOWL, unidentified.

Lent by Mrs. B. Franklin Mechling.

SUGAR TONGS, marked N.C.

Lent by Mrs. Richard Waln Meirs.

TWO SALT SPOONS, unidentified. Belonged to Mary Cocke Morison, great grandmother.

Lent by Miss Sarah Agnes Morison.

SOUP TUREEN WITH LID, unidentified. This was given to the second cousin of Mrs. Morris' grandfather, Edward Shippen, by Mrs. Edward Shippen Burd who inherited it from her husband. The inscription reads: "A tribute of gratitude and affection from Elizabeth Powel to her valued relative and efficient legal friend. Edward Shippen Burd, May 27th, 1825." Mrs. Morris' grandmother inherited the tray from her husband, Edward Shippen and before her death gave it to Roland S. Morris.

SALVER, unidentified. This was part of a silver service presented to Commodore Stephen Decatur, her third great uncle, by the City of Philadelphia to commemorate his conquests in the Mediterranean. The inscription reads:

"By Citizens of Philadelphia
    To their Townsman
        Commodore Decatur
            Estimed for his virtue
                Honored for his valour."

There is no date on the tray but it was presumably presented to him on his return to Philadelphia in January, 1816.

Lent by Mrs. Roland S. Morris.

MUG, unidentified.

Lent by Mrs. R. Wilson McCredy.

SUGAR TONGS, unidentified.

> Lent by Mrs. Walter S. McInnes.

SUGAR SIFTER, marked I.B., unidentified. American, c. 1770. Belonged to her great, great grandfather, Israel Whelen (1752–1806). He married Mary Downing of Downington. Israel Whelen was Commissary General under Washington, Financial agent signing Continental Currency, State Senator and Elector when John Adams became president. His son, Israel, was the father of her mother's father, Henry Whelen, Senior.

> Lent by Mrs. Thornton Oakley.

SUGAR BOWL, unidentified. It is made from a cocoanut shell.

> Lent by Miss Ella Parsons.

SALT SPOON, unidentified. Engraved "R.S."

> Lent by Mrs. Henry D. Paxson, deceased.

CREAMER, unidentified. Belonged to Margaret Fisher Barrett, a descendant of Thomas and Margery Maud Fisher.

CREAMER, unidentified. Original owner, Elizabeth Montgomery, of Wilmington, Delaware.

FORKS, unidentified. Original owner, Mary Shellcross Lovering, of "Hope Farm," Wilmington, Delaware.

VEGETABLE SPOONS, unidentified. Original owner, Elizabeth Cowgill Corbit, a descendant of Ellen Cowgill who was a passenger on "The Welcome" with William Penn.

FILLING SPOON, unidentified. Original owner, Francis Rawle.

SUGAR SHAKER, unidentified. Original owners, Thomas and Anna Clifford.

SHELL LADLE, unidentified. Original owner, Sarah Lovering.

> Lent by Mrs. Henry Pemberton, Jr.

TABLESPOON, marked R.W. in oval, 1800–1810.   Coffin handle.

TABLESPOONS, PAIR, unidentified, 1790–1810.   Stags head crest.

TEASPOON, marked W. P. in rectangle, 1800.
    Lent by Mrs. Charles W. Perkins.

SUGAR SIFTER, unidentified.   Belonged to John Taylor (1721–1761).
    Lent by Mrs. James DeWolf Perry.

SAUCE BOAT AND LADLE, unidentified.

SPOON, unidentified.   Said to have been given to Rebecca Cornell, wife of Clement Cornell Biddle, by Light Horse Harry Lee.
    Lent by Mrs. William R. Philler.

*OVAL SNUFF BOX, no makers marks, probably American. Engraved M. Rutter, 1750.   She was Mary Catherine Ghiselin Rutter, daughter of Cesar Ghiselin, one of the earliest goldsmiths working in Philadelphia.   She married for her second husband, William Pyewell, July 24, 1735.   Their daughter, Rebecca Pyewell, married John Phillips, April 10, 1766.   Their son, William Phillips, married Anna Smith, April 29, 1799.   Their son, Clements Stocker Phillips, married Mary Brinton, October 25, 1838.   Their son, Clement Stocker Phillips, married Anna Clifford Biddle, November 15, 1881.   Their daughter, Phoebe Caroline Phillips, married Alfred Coxe Prime, June 14, 1922.
    Lent by Mrs. Alfred Coxe Prime.

TEAPOT, marked W.H.

PAIR OF TEASPOONS, marked W.M.B.
    Lent by Mrs. B. Brannan Reath, II.

TEAPOT, marked J.S., 1772.
    Lent by Miss Lydia Wistar Rhoads.

Spoon, unidentified. Belonged to Mary Jane Ashurst, great, great, great aunt of the present owner.

Lent by Miss Mary Leiper Rhoad.

Sugar Tongs, unidentified, c. 1760.

Lent by Mrs. Henry B. Robb.

*Marrow Spoon, marked A.B. This belonged to Mrs. Robb's great, great grandfather, Nathaniel Mitchell. In 1780–81 he was Brigade Major. He was a Prisoner of War on Parole in 1782; delegate to the First Continental Congress in Delaware, 1786–88; Governor of Delaware, 1805–1808, and a member of the Delaware Society of the Cincinnati.

Lent by Mrs. Henry B. Robb.

*Pap Bowl, unidentified. Belonged to her maternal ancestors, the Markoe's, and has the Markoe crest and "M." engraved on it.

*Wine Syphon, unidentified.

Lent by Miss Emilie M. Rivinus.

Sugar Bowl, unidentified. Gallery and pineapple finial. Belonged to an aunt of Mr. Sargent's who lived in Philadelphia.

Lent by Mrs. Winthrop Sargent.

Bowl, unidentified. American.

Lent by Mrs. Joseph W. Shannon.

*One Dozen Pistol-Handled Knives and Forks in Case, unidentified. Belonged to Josiah Langdale and Mary Morrison Coates, married July 16, 1772. Marked T.S.

Lent by Mrs. Joseph W. Sharp, Jr.

Six Spoons, marked G.H. Originally owned by Mary Ann Rinehart, 1750, who was the great, great grandmother of Boyd Lee Spahr. They were inherited by Sarah Ellen Rinehart, 1786, great grandmother; Mary

Ann Rockafellow, 1820, great aunt; Sarah Ellen Koser, 1855, aunt; who presented them to Miss Katharine Febiger on her marriage to Boyd Lee Spahr.

Lent by Mrs. Boyd Lee Spahr.

*CREAMER, unidentified. c. 1790.

Lent by Mrs. Alfred Stengel.

COFFEE POT, CREAM BOWL, SUGAR BOWL, TEAPOT and WASTE BOWL, unidentified. Belonged to Rebecca Talbot, Providence, R. I.

CREAM LADLE, unidentified.

PITCHER, unidentified.

STOCK BUCKLES, unidentified. Engraved "P.F."

SUGAR TONGS, unidentified.

SUGAR TONGS, unidentified. Engraved "G.R.T." Belonged to Gustavus Taylor who married Rebecca Talbot in 1790.

TWO TEASPOONS, marked I.B. Engraved S.A.

Lent by Mr. and Mrs. Arnold Gindrat Talbot.

CHATELAINE, unidentified. American, 18th Century. Belonged to Barbara Clark, of Savannah, Georgia, about 1798, who married Abram Gindrat in 1803.

Lent by Miss Frances Katharine Talbot.

CREAMER, unidentified. Belonged to her great, great grandmother, Deborah Kirkham.

Lent by Mrs. Richard P. Tatum.

SUGAR TONGS, marked "W.W."

Lent by Mrs. J. Madison Taylor.

TABLESPOONS, marked H.O.&F. with bright cutting. Engraved "1782, J.S.W." for John and Sarah Warner.

SUGAR TONGS, unmarked. Engraved "1814." Part of the wedding silver of Lydia Fisher who married Benjamin Warner, September 22, 1814.

Lent by Miss Lydia Fisher Warner.

MINIATURE TEASPOONS AND SUGAR TONGS, unidentified. Inherited from her grandmother, Rebecca Neal McPherson, of Alexandria, Virginia, who married Pennell Palmer.

SPOON, unidentified.   Rat tail.
> Lent by Mrs. Carroll Williams.

CREAMER, unidentified.   American.
> Lent by Mrs. James W. Wister.

PORRINGER, mark erased, "M.E." original owner, lent by Mrs. Horatio Curtis Wood.

FEEDING BOAT, unidentified.   Belonged to great, great grandmother, Humphreys.

JUNKET SPOON, unidentified.

KNITTING NEEDLE CASE, unidentified.   Belonged to great, great grandmother, Humphreys.

MUG WITH SPOUT, unidentified.

PIN CUSHION WITH SILVER BAND, unidentified.   Belonged to great, great grandmother, Humphreys.

SMALL PUNCH LADLE WITH WHALE-BONE HANDLE, unidentified.

PAIR OF SALT CELLARS, unmarked.

PAIR OF SALT SPOONS, unmarked.

SUGAR TONGS, unidentified.

TABLESPOONS, marked W.H.

*PAIR OF TABLESPOONS WITH FEATHER EDGE, marked I.C.
> Lent by Miss Margaret E. Wright and Miss Hannah C. Wright.

1. JOSEPH ANTHONY, JR. (1762–1814), Philadelphia Silversmith. From the original by Gilbert Stuart; courtesy of the Metropolitan Museum of Art.

2. I. BAILEY, Ladle; JOHN DAVID, Creamer; HARVEY LEWIS, Teapot and Sauce Boat; Unidentified, Spoon; lent by Miss Lydia Fisher Warner.

3. WILLIAM BALL, Creamer; DANIEL VAN VOORHIS, Sugar Urn with lid missing; lent by Mrs. Charles C. Perkins.

8. BROWNE & HOULTON, Creamer; lent by Mrs. Evan Randolph.

4. ADRIAN BANCKER, Tankard; lent by Mr. and Mrs. Harrold E. Gillingham.

5. STANDISH BARRY, Teapot; owned by Mrs. May Stevenson Easby.

11. CHAUDRON & RASCH, Coffee Pot and Teapot; JOEL SAYRE, Sugar Bowl and Creamer; lent by Mrs. W. Clarke Grieb.

9. BROWNE & SEALE, Beaker; JOHN LETELIER, Bowl; lent by Mrs. Alfred Coxe Prime.

6. WILLIAM BARTRAM, Salver and Salt-cellars, pair; lent by Mrs. Alfred Coxe Prime.

12. SILVER LOAN EXHIBIT, December 8-11, 1937. House of the Colonial Dames, 1630 Latimer Street. Over seven hundred pieces were shown.

23. JOHN GERMON, Salt Spoons, pair; JOHN JENKINS, Mustard Spoon; lent by Mr. and Mrs. Christian Febiger.

24. WILLIAM GHISELIN, Creamer; courtesy of The Philadelphia Museum of Art.

26. DAVID HALL, Coffee Pot; lent by Mrs. John W. Pepper, deceased. Now owned by Miss Caroline D. Bache.

25. WILLIAM GHISELIN, Porringer; lent by Mrs. Walter T. Moore.

28. WILLIAM HOLLINGSHEAD, Creamer; lent by Mrs. William W. Doughten.

30. WILLIAM HOLMES, Porringer with keyhole handle; owned by the family of the late William Rotch Wister.

31. JAMES HOWELL & COMPANY, Coffee Pot; owned by Mrs. May Stevenson Easby.

32. RICHARD HUMPHREYS, Can; owned by Mrs. May Stevenson Easby.

27. THOMAS HAMERSLEY, Tankard; lent by Mr. Joseph Carson; PHILIP SYNG, JR., Coffee Pot; lent by Mrs. Thomas Evans.

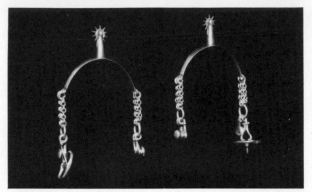

33. RICHARD HUMPHREYS, Spurs; owned by Mr. Lawrence
J. Morris.

34. RICHARD HUMPHREYS,
Coffee Pot; lent by Dr. James
Alan Montgomery.

35. RICHARD HUMPHREYS,
Dress Sword; owned by Mr.
Lawrence J. Morris.

37. JACOB HURD, Pap Boat; owned by the family of the late William
Rotch Wister.

38. JACOB HURD, Porringer with keyhole handle; lent by Mrs. H. Norris Harrison.

39. CORNELIUS KIERSTEADE, Tankard; lent by Mrs. Campbell Madeira, deceased.

29. WILLIAM HOLLINGSHEAD, Can; owned by Miss Essyllt Evans. JOSEPH RICHARDSON, JR., Goblet; owned by Miss Mary Evans.

36. RICHARD HUMPHREYS, Strainer; JOSEPH RICHARDSON, JR., Can; lent by Miss Hannah C. and Miss Margaret E. Wright.

41. HARVEY LEWIS, Coffee Pot, Creamer and Sugar Bowl; Unmarked, Sugar Tongs; lent by Miss Lydia Fisher Warner.

40. CHARLES LE ROUX, Sauce Boats, pair, with French characteristics; lent by Mr. Robert R. Logan.

42. LEWIS & SMITH, Creamer and Sugar Urn; lent by Mr. and Mrs. Harrold E. Gillingham.

43. JOHN LEACOCK, Sugar Bowl; JOSEPH RICHARDSON, Tray; lent by Mr. Robert R. Logan.

44. JOSEPH LOWNES, Waste Bowl; owned by Mrs. May Stevenson Easby.

45. JOSEPH LOWNES, Bowl; owned by Mr. May Stevenson Easby.

46. JOSEPH LOWNES, Sugar Urn; owned by
Mrs. May Stevenson Easby.

47. JOSEPH LOWNES, Can; lent by Mrs.
Frank B. Gummey.

48. JOSEPH LOWNES, Creamer, Waste Bowl and Teapot; lent by Mr. and Mrs. Christian Febiger.

49. JOSEPH LOWNES, Ladle; lent by Mrs. Henry B. Robb

50. JOSEPH LOWNES, Tankard; lent by Mr. Samuel J. Henderson.

51. JOSEPH LOWNES, Coffee Pot and Water Pitcher; lent by Mr. and Mrs. Christian Febiger.

52. JOSEPH LOWNES, from a copy of the original portrait; owned by Mr. Wistar Harvey.

53. JOHN LYNCH, Coffee Pot; owned by Mrs. Joseph Harrison. The lid lifts out.

56. EDMUND MILNE, Porringer with keyhole handle; owned by the family of the late William Rotch Wister.

54. JOHN McMULLIN, Creamer and Sugar Bowl; lent by Mrs. Alfred Coxe Prime.

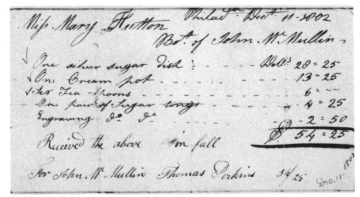

55. JOHN McMULLIN, Bill for Creamer and Sugar Bowl; lent by Mrs. Alfred Coxe Prime.

57. EDMUND MILNE, Brandy Warmer; lent by Mrs. Thornton Oakley.

58. MOORE & FERGUSON, Creamer; JACOBUS VANDERSPIEGEL, Tankard; lent by Mrs. Horatio C. Wood.

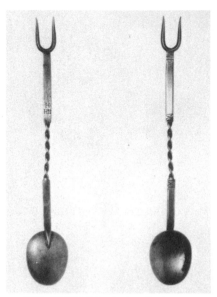

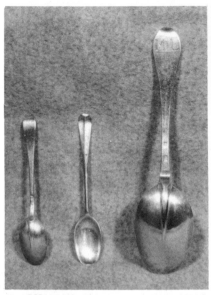

59. JOHANNIS NYS, Sucket Fork; courtesy of The Philadelphia Museum of Art; given to the Museum by Mrs. Alfred Coxe Prime.

60. JOHANNIS NYS, Spoon; PHILIP SYNG, II, Small Spoons, two; lent by Mr. Robert R. Logan.

61. JOHANNIS NYS, Tankard; made for George and Mary Emlen in 1717; lent by The Historical Society of Pennsylvania.

62. JOHANNIS NYS, Porringer; lent by Mrs. Arthur Howell.

65. SAMUEL PANCOAST, Sugar Urn; lent by Mrs. William Wistar Comfort.

66. SAMUEL PANCOAST, Creamer; lent by Mrs. Raymond Shortlidge.

63. JOHANNIS NYS, Porringers, pair; lent by Dr. George Morrison Coates.

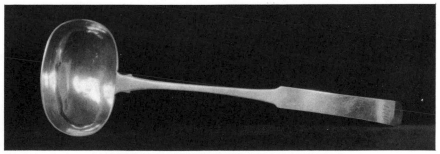

64. JESSE OWEN, Ladle; lent by Miss Xenia Clampitt.

67. PAUL REVERE, Coffee Urn, Sugar Urn and Teapot with stand; owned by Miss Frances Porter and Mrs. William Stanley Parker.

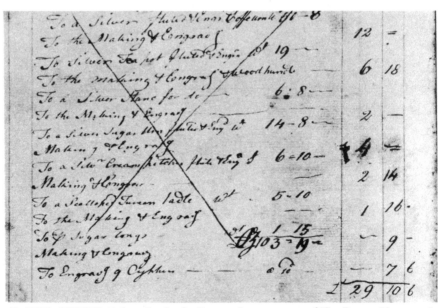

68. PAUL REVERE, Ledger Entries for Revere pieces; courtesy of The Boston Museum of Fine Arts.

69. FRANCIS RICHARDSON, Porringer; lent by
Mrs. William W. Doughten.

72. FRANCIS RICHARDSON, II., Porringer;
lent by Mr. and Mrs. C. Jared Ingersoll.

70. FRANCIS RICHARDSON, Porringer; lent
by Mrs. David Buzby Robb.

73. JOSEPH RICHARDSON, SR., Hot Milk Can with original spout; owned by Mr. J. Robeson Howell.

74. JOSEPH RICHARDSON, SR., Sugar Bowl with Cypher; lent by Mrs. Charles A. Fife.

75. JOSEPH RICHARDSON, SR., Salver with maker's mark on edge; lent by Mrs. Francis von A. Cabeen.

71. FRANCIS RICHARDSON, Tankard; lent by Dr. Isaac Starr.

76. JOSEPH RICHARDSON, SR., Teapot; lent by Mr. Robert R. Logan.

77. JOSEPH RICHARDSON, SR., Hot Water Can; owned by Miss Martha Paul Howell.

78. JOSEPH RICHARDSON, SR., Porringer with keyhole handle; Unidentified, Strainer (probably foreign); lent by Mrs. Joseph B. Hutchinson.

79. JOSEPH RICHARDSON, SR., Coffee Pot with coat of arms; lent by Miss Hannah C. and Miss Margaret E. Wright; ROBERT SWAN, Coffee Pot; lent by Mrs. Joseph W. Shannon.

80. JOSEPH RICHARDSON, JR., Doll's Teaspoons and Sugar Tongs; Unidentified, Sugar Bowl, marked R. P.; lent by Miss Clarissa T. Chase.

81. JOSEPH RICH-ARDSON, JR., Silver Gilt Spoons; lent by Mr. Lawrence J. Morris.

82. JOSEPH RICHARDSON, JR., Nutmeg Grater, open and closed; owned by Mr. Lawrence J. Morris.

83. JOSEPH RICHARDSON, JR., Helmet Creamer; lent by Mr. and Mrs. Harrold E. Gillingham.

84. JOSEPH RICHARDSON, JR., Tea Service; lent by Mrs. George D. Fowle.

85. JOSEPH RICHARDSON, JR., Teapots, two; lent by Mrs. William Norton Johnson.

86. JOSEPH RICHARDSON, JR., Bill for Silver; owned by Mrs. William Norton Johnson.

87. JOSEPH RICHARDSON, JR., Sauce Boat; owned by Mr. Lawrence J. Morris.

88. JOSEPH RICHARDSON, JR., Tankard; lent by Miss Augusta McMillan.

90. JOSEPH & NATHANIEL RICH-ARDSON, Coffee Pot; lent by Mrs. Charles E. Ingersoll.

89. JOSEPH RICHARDSON, JR., Dome-lidded Sugar Bowl and Sugar Tongs; lent by Mrs. William Norton Johnson. (Mentioned in bill on Page 161.)

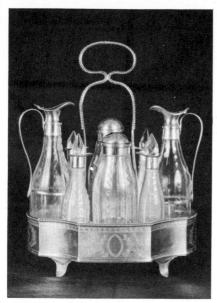

93. GODFREY SHIVING, Castor Set; lent by Mrs. Stanley Eyre Wilson.

91. THOMAS SHIELDS, Can; lent by Mr. and Mrs. Christian Febiger.

92. THOMAS SHIELDS, Can; ENGLISH, Tankard, 1752; lent by Miss Lydia Fisher Warner.

95. PHILIP SYNG, II, Salver; lent by Mr. W. Clarke Hanna.

94. JOHN STOW, Tankard; lent by Mrs. Walter M. Jeffords.

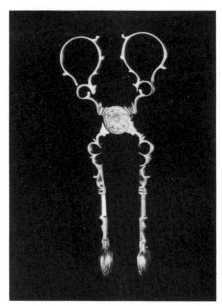

96. PHILIP SYNG, II, Sugar Nippers; lent by Miss Clarissa T. Chase.

97. PHILIP SYNG, II, Salver; lent by Mr. and Mrs. C. Jared Ingersoll.

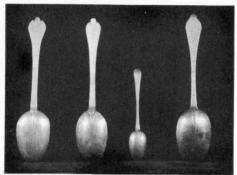

98. PHILIP SYNG, II, Small Spoon; ENGLISH Spoons, three; lent by Mr. and Mrs. Harrold E. Gillingham.

99. PHILIP SYNG, II, Spoons; lent by Mr. Robert R. Logan.

Received November 16: 1769 of Mary Coates Three Pounds Eight Shillings for 1 Silver Cream Pott w: is in full of all demands

Phil: Syng

£3. 8s

100. PHILIP SYNG, II, Bill for Creamer, below; owned by Mr. Lawrence J. Morris.

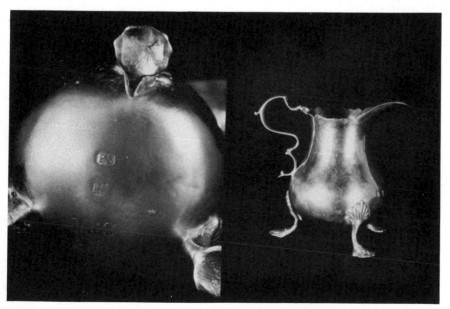

101. PHILIP SYNG, II, Creamer with maker's mark; owned by Mr. Lawrence J. Morris.

104. PHILIP SYNG, II, Bowl; lent by Mrs. Raymond Shortlidge.

103. PHILIP SYNG, II, (1703–1789); lent by Mrs. Raymond Shortlidge.

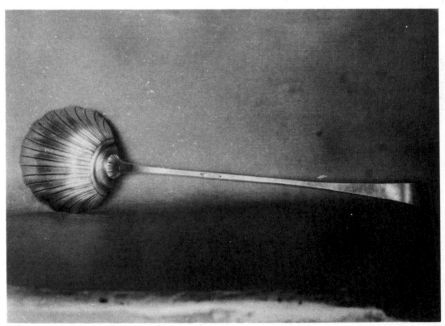

102. PHILIP SYNG, II, Ladle (the unusual mark is reproduced in silversmiths' list); owned by Mr. Philip Syng Justice.

107. SAMUEL VERNON, Porringer; owned
by the family of the late William Rotch Wister.

106. JOHN VERNON, Sugar Urn (attributed);
lent by Mrs. Roland Whitridge.

105. JACOBUS VANDERSPIEGEL, Trencher Salts, lent by Mrs. James de W. Cookman; courtesy
of The Gallery of Fine Arts, Yale University.

110. WILLIAM VILANT, Tankard; courtesy of The Philadelphia Museum of Art.

108. SAMUEL VERNON, Pepper Pot; lent by Mrs. William Wistar Comfort.

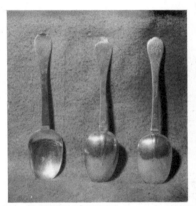

109. SAMUEL VERNON, Spoon (middle); lent by Mr. and Mrs. Arnold Gindrat Talbot. ENGLISH Spoons, two; lent by Miss Lydia W. Rhoads.

111. WILLIAM VILANT, Tankard; lent by Dr. George Morrison Coates.

113. CHRISTIAN WILTBERGER, Sugar Urn; lent by Mrs. Daniel M. Shewbrooks.

112. WHARTENBY & BUMM, Wine Cooler; lent by The Historical Society of Pennsylvania.

114. CHRISTIAN WILTBERGER, Waste Bowl; ENGLISH Salver and Teapot; Unidentified Creamer; lent by Mrs. Alfred Stengel.

115. EDWARD WINSLOW, Porringer; lent
by Mrs. William Wistar Comfort.

116. BANCROFT WOODCOCK, Can; lent by
Mr. Lardner Howell.

117. BANCROFT WOODCOCK, Sugar Bowl;
lent by The Philadelphia Museum of Art.

118. JOHN WAITE, Spoon; ENGLISH Spoon;
Unidentified; lent by Mrs. William Wistar
Comfort.

119. CASE OF EARLY AMERICAN SILVER. (English tray, lower right.)

120. CAUDLE CUP, 1675, London; probably by John Sutton; lent by Mrs. Evan Randolph.

121. POMANDER, c. 1700-1720 open; SNUFF BOX, American, back; lent by Mrs. Alfred Coxe Prime.

122. POMANDER, c. 1700–1720, closed; SNUFF BOX, American, back; lent by Mrs. Alfred Coxe Prime.

123. SALVER, 1720–1736; made by Thomas Mason; lent by Mr. Robert R. Logan.

125. KETTLE AND STAND, London; Kettle
by George Wickes, 1752. Stand, 1750-51; lent
by Miss Alice M. Prime.

126. SALVER, 1744; lent by Miss Alice M.
Prime.

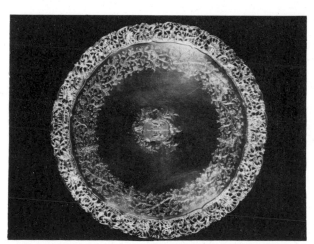

128. SALVER, Robert Rew, 1762; lent by Mrs. Edwin Schenck.

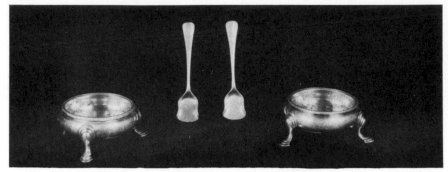

127. SALT CELLARS AND SPOONS, William Plummer, 1755; lent by Mrs. W. Goodell Clark.

129. CANDLESTICKS, London, 1763, Thomas Black;
lent by Mrs. Addinell Hewson; Unidentified PISTOL
HANDLED KNIVES AND FORKS; lent by Mrs.
Joseph W. Sharp, Jr.

131. TEAPOT STAND, 1771, John Carter;
Creamer, 1774; lent by Mrs. Alfred Coxe Prime.

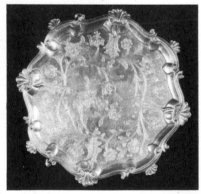

130. SALVER, Thomas Hannam and
Richard Mills, 1764; lent by Mrs. Francis
von A. Cabeen.

132. TEAPOT AND SUGAR BOWL, Richard Gurney & Company, 1750; lent by Mrs. Meredith Hanna.

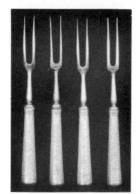

133. FORKS, Richard Tudor, 1773; lent by Mrs. Andrew W. Crawford.

134. KNIVES, Richard Tudor, 1773; lent by Mrs. Andrew W. Crawford.

124. BRANDY WARMER, London, 1731; lent by Mrs. Alfred Coxe Prime.

137. MOTE SPOON, Unidentified (two views); lent by Mrs. Francis von A. Cabeen.

138. WINE SYPHON AND PAP BOWL, Unidentified; lent by Miss Emilie Rivinus. Other articles not exhibited.

136. CAKE BASKET, DUTCH; owned by Mr. May Stevenson Easby.

135. SALVER, FRENCH; owned by
Mr. May Stevenson Easby.

139. MARROW SPOON, marked
A.B., Unidentified; lent by Mrs.
Henry B. Robb.

140. SPOON, marked I. C., Unidentified; lent by Miss Hannah C.
and Miss Margaret E. Wright.

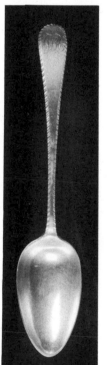

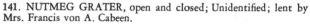

141. NUTMEG GRATER, open and closed; Unidentified; lent by
Mrs. Francis von A. Cabeen.

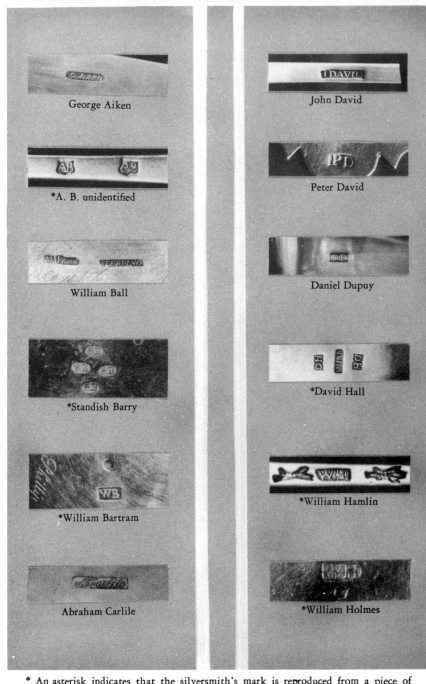

George Aiken

*A. B. unidentified

William Ball

*Standish Barry

*William Bartram

Abraham Carlile

John David

Peter David

Daniel Dupuy

*David Hall

*William Hamlin

*William Holmes

* An asterisk indicates that the silversmith's mark is reproduced from a piece of silver exhibited.

*Houlton & Browne

J. Howell

Richard Humphreys

*Jacob Hurd

*Hurd (Jacob)

*John Leacock

*Charles Le Roux

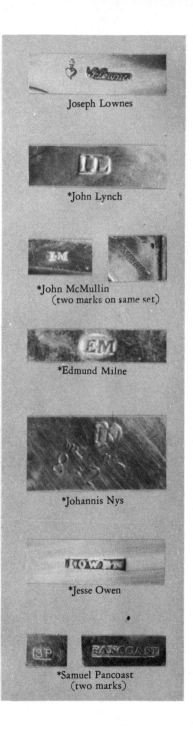

Joseph Lownes

*John Lynch

*John McMullin
(two marks on same set)

*Edmund Milne

*Johannis Nys

*Jesse Owen

*Samuel Pancoast
(two marks)

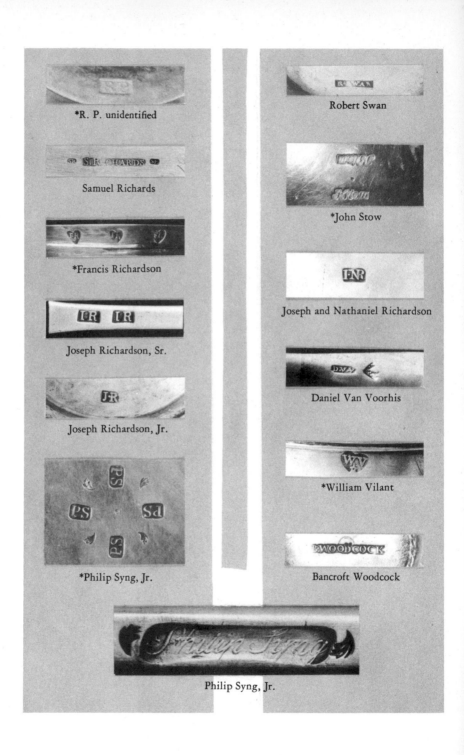

*R. P. unidentified

Samuel Richards

*Francis Richardson

Joseph Richardson, Sr.

Joseph Richardson, Jr.

*Philip Syng, Jr.

Robert Swan

*John Stow

Joseph and Nathaniel Richardson

Daniel Van Voorhis

*William Vilant

Bancroft Woodcock

Philip Syng, Jr.

LIST OF ILLUSTRATIONS

PAGE

190 Three Centuries of

PAGE

124. BRANDY WARMER, London, 1731; lent by Mrs. Alfred Coxe Prime ... 175
125. KETTLE AND STAND, London; Kettle by George Wickes, 1752. Stand, 1750–51; lent by Miss Alice M. Prime ... 173
126. SALVER, 1744; lent by Miss Alice M. Prime ... 173
127. SALT CELLARS AND SPOONS, William Plummer, 1755; lent by Mrs. W. Goodell Clark ... 174
128. SALVER, Robert Rew, 1762; lent by Mrs. Edwin Schenck ... 173
129. CANDLESTICKS, London, 1763, Thomas Black; lent by Mrs. Addinell Hewson. Unidentified, Pistol Handled Knives and Forks; lent by Mrs. Joseph W. Sharp, Jr. ... 174
130. SALVER, Thomas Hannam and Richard Mills, 1764; lent by Mrs. Francis von A. Cabeen ... 174
131. TEAPOT STAND, 1771, John Carter; CREAMER, 1774; lent by Mrs. Alfred Coxe Prime ... 174
132. TEAPOT AND SUGAR BOWL, Richard Gurney & Company, 1750; lent by Mrs. Meredith Hanna ... 175
133. FORKS, Richard Tudor, 1773; lent by Mrs. Andrew W. Crawford ... 175
134. KNIVES, Richard Tudor, 1773; lent by Mrs. Andrew W. Crawford ... 175
135. SALVER, French; owned by Mr. May Stevenson Easby ... 178
136. CAKE BASKET, Dutch; owned by Mr. May Stevenson Easby ... 177
137. MOTE SPOON, Unidentified, two views; lent by Mrs. Francis von A. Cabeen ... 177
138. WINE SYPHON AND PAP BOWL, Unidentified;

One thousand copies of "Three Centuries of Historic Silver" have been printed.

This copy is number *655*.